THE OBSERVER'S
POCKET SERIES

THE OBSERVER'S BOOK OF
WEATHER ✦ ✦ ✦

The Observer's Books

THE OBSERVER'S BOOK OF

WEATHER

By
REGINALD M. LESTER
F.R. Met. Soc.

FREDERICK WARNE & CO. LTD.
FREDERICK WARNE & CO. INC.
LONDON · NEW YORK

CONTENTS

ACKNOWLEDGEMENTS

Plates 2, 3, 4, 5, 6, 7, 9, 10, 12, 13, 15, 16, 19, 30, 34 are reproduced by permission of the Royal Meteorological Society (from the Clarke Collection).

Plates 48, 51, 53, 55, 58 and 61 (upper) are reproduced by permission of British European Airways.

Plates 49, 56, 59 and 60 are reproduced by permission of Odhams Press.

The publishers are also indebted to the following for permission to reproduce works illustrated:

Air Ministry (Plate 50); Barratt's Photo Press Ltd. (Plate 61, lower); Controller of H.M. Stationery Office (Crown copyright) (Plate 52); Keystone Press Agency Ltd. (Plate 62); R. W. Munro Ltd. (Plate 45); A. Ronald Traube (Plate 25); Negretti & Zambra Ltd (Plate 44).

INTRODUCTION

WEATHER is a subject of never-ending interest and conversation. Who can fail to be thrilled by the magnificent pageantry of the clouds, or the wonderful colourings of sunsets and other sky phenomena?

But there is also the practical side, for weather has a very big influence on industry and health. It is, perhaps, surprising to find that almost every industry is so much affected by it. Agriculture, shipping, aviation and all kinds of transport are dependent on weather conditions. In the business world, temperature and humidity will affect such things as the control of air-conditioning plants, the making of stencils for typewriters, food supplies to restaurants, etc. Ice-cream companies call for weather forecasts to determine their day-to-day production; building firms and contractors, fuel companies, departmental stores and so on, all need weather reports for the successful operation of their concerns.

On an equally large scale, weather has an important bearing on people's pleasure in the direction of sports and entertainments. An increasingly wide use is being made of the personal services supplied to private individuals by the Meteorological Office, as anyone may telephone for a forecast for any particular area at any hour of the day or night. Enquiries are made about the probable coming weather conditions for yachting, cricket, polo, fishing, flying and all types of sports.

During 1962 there was a 28 per cent increase in the number of civilian weather enquiries at the information centres in London, Manchester, Glasgow and Southampton, where 415,310 were dealt with during the twelve months. London alone handled 253,833 enquiries. On one day, during the December fog, there were over 2,500 telephone calls.

Any member of the public may 'phone for a weather forecast by dialling the numbers given in their local telephone directories under the heading "WEATHER."

Enquiries for weather forecasts from the building industry increased by well over 150 per cent between 1962 and 1967, and general enquiries by over 50 per cent.

The most recent service in this direction is for building contractors to be able to make an allowance, when preparing tenders, for the time likely to be lost on the contract due to adverse weather. The service is called *Climest*, and provides month by month estimates of the probability of periods of moderate or heavy rain, strong winds and low temperatures for any area of the country.

We have seen how a tropical hurricane and other major storms of a similar nature have created a greater devastation and loss of life than some of the biggest air raids of the last war. Even in this country we have had in recent years examples of exceptional storms that have caused widespread havoc and casualties, such as the Lynmouth storm of 1952 and the North Sea floods of 1953.

The importance of weather research cannot, therefore, be over-estimated, and in this respect not only the official meteorologist but the amateur observer has a big part to play.

CHAPTER I

EXPLORING INTO SPACE

THOSE of us who were in southern England during the latter part of the last war have very unhappy memories of the V2 rocket, which we still think of as a weapon of destruction only. But when the war ended, these rockets were turned to constructive use. They were sent up into the higher altitudes to collect valuable information about the atmosphere at those great heights beyond the reach of man. Indeed, they have now penetrated into outer space itself.

Until about 1945 the highest altitude records obtained were from V2 rockets in America, which penetrated up to about 450,000 feet. Today the earth's envelope is being explored to distances of hundreds of miles by means of rockets and satellites. The Meteorological Office cannot afford costly high atmosphere exploration as part of its general work, but the Committee for Space Research uses artificial earth satellites as platforms for observing the weather downwards from outside the atmosphere.

The American Tiros series, followed by the new Nimbus series, are the only launchings of satellites primarily for weather research, but a member of the Meteorological Office from Britain is attached to the satellite group of the U.S. Weather Bureau.

Before we start to study the weather over the lower levels of the earth's surface, we should have some acquaintance with these higher regions of the atmosphere which extend outward from the earth's surface like a gaseous envelope to (so far as we know at present) a depth of about 200 miles.

The two principal layers of which our atmosphere

is composed are known as the stratosphere and the troposphere. The troposphere is the lower layer, which stretches from the earth's surface to the beginning of the stratosphere. The latter varies in height in different parts of the world and according to prevailing weather conditions. It has its greatest altitude over the equator, where it is sometimes as high as 12 miles, and its lowest over the two poles, where it has been known to be as low as 6 miles above the earth.

We do not yet know how high the atmosphere actually extends, but it has been established that the limit of twilight—i.e. the point where the shadow of the earth which the sun casts on the sky after passing below the horizon, or before rising above it—is about 49 miles high, and that the observation of meteor trails suggests that atmosphere exists up to some 200 miles above the earth. It is probable, however, that it stretches to even greater heights, as there must be some atmosphere to make auroral streamers visible (and these have been measured to exceed 300 miles in altitude). Where space actually begins (such as we know "space," devoid of all atmosphere), still remains to be solved.

The way in which weather conditions in the troposphere affect the level of the stratosphere is when a storm of exceptional violence has the effect of lifting the stratosphere several miles higher than normal. Generally, however, very little weather is encountered more than about 8 or 9 miles above the earth, and there are very few clouds higher than 7 miles.

It will be understood, therefore, how the stratosphere, being free of complex weather conditions, is an ideal area for air travel. There are, however, certain dangers to air travel in the stratosphere,

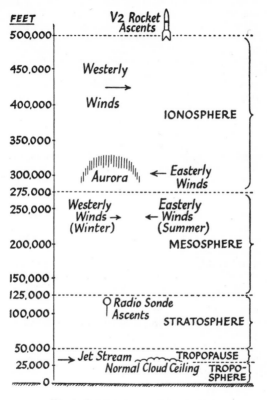

Fig. i. LAYERS OF THE ATMOSPHERE

particularly from cosmic radiation.* It has been found that the cosmic rays about 14 miles up are 150 times stronger than at earth-level. When cosmic rays reach such a force they could crush to death both man and his machine.

The stratosphere also protects our earth from the bombardment of meteorites, and it is only very occasionally that one of these meteorites will break through this defence and hit the earth. Even then they are usually of a small variety, the only major one of the present century being the Great Meteor of 1908, which luckily struck an uninhabited part of the earth in the wastes of Siberia. If it had crashed through the stratosphere about 4 hours later, it would have wiped out entirely the whole city of Leningrad. It laid waste about 8,000 square kilometres of forest; the explosion was seen 275 miles away, and the heat was felt for 40 miles.

The atmosphere surrounding our earth also protects us from the intense cold of the upper regions by acting as a kind of blanket that is able to retain the sun's heat.

It has only been possible to investigate these higher regions through recording the travel of sound waves from explosions that have reached such heights, and then been reflected back to earth by the rising temperature.

The behaviour of the temperature as one ascends through these different spheres—or layers—is both interesting and surprising. We usually believe that temperature falls as height increases. This is generally the case in the troposphere, and at the base

* Those who have made high ascents in balloons or aeroplanes have found that there is a radiation, obviously generated in outer space, and believed to be due to charged particles moving at very high velocities, and which emits very penetrating rays. A tremendous amount of research into cosmic rays has been going on for many years, and still continues, as there is much more about these rays that scientists yet require to know.

4

of the stratosphere it is from 50° to 100° below zero F. Contrary to what we would expect, it is much colder at that height over the tropics than over the temperate zone. About 10 miles up, a temperature of 133° below zero F. (165 degrees of frost) has been recorded over the equator by an air pilot.

But when we reach the stratosphere, a slow upward incline of temperature begins. At the ceiling of the stratosphere (about 125,000 feet), it is from 50 to 75 degrees warmer than at the base, and it goes on rising up to about 160,000 feet, where the meso-peak starts and where temperatures of over 100°F. have been recorded.

At that stage, a new decline starts, and the temperature falls steadily until the ceiling of the meso-sphere (about 260,000 feet) is reached. This is probably the deepest minimum attained (somewhere around 120° below zero F.). But from here upwards there is a steady rise, and it is believed that above these man-discovered heights the temperature becomes excessively hot, and may reach anything up to 4,000°F.

Apart from temperature, there are other observations of great interest in these different layers above the earth. One of these, which undoubtedly has an important bearing on our weather below, is the behaviour of the winds.

Aircraft pilots occasionally encounter some quite alarming narrow belts of high-speed winds, with velocities of nearly 300 m.p.h., near the base of the stratosphere. They are sometimes hundreds of miles long, and aircraft can make no headway at all against them. It has been noticed that they are strongest over the eastern sides of continents where continental air masses (referred to later in this chapter) meet maritime air masses of a different temperature.

5

Generally, the wind strength increases as we ascend through the troposphere. Owing to the fact that just below the stratosphere base there is an immense low-pressure area centred round the North Pole, where the winds circulate anti-clockwise, they are mainly westerly here, irrespective of what direction they are blowing at the earth's surface. At a height of about 120,000 feet to 160,000 feet, the winds are westerly in winter and easterly in summer. In the ionosphere, easterly winds predominate in the lower region, and westerly above about 400,000 feet.

Research is also being carried on into conditions in the ionosphere—the electrically charged layer in the atmosphere that plays such a large part in long-distance radio communication. Important research also has to be carried out on ultra-violet radiation and ozone extending beyond the stratosphere into the mesosphere. (See Fig. i.) An ozonesonde is now being manufactured for ozone studies, and the latest instrument to have passed its trials is a phosphorus pentoxide balloon-borne hygrometer, designed by P. Goldsmith of Harwell.

One other interesting series of observations has been made, and that is the changing of the sky colouring at different stages of an ascent. This data was first recorded by the American National Geographic-Army Stratosphere Expedition. The observers noticed that the colour of the sky changed gradually from the familiar light blue to a dim purple and finally to a greyish black. The colours and other observations at different heights are shown on Plate i, and in Fig. i.

Research into these upper regions is going ahead continuously. The results may eventually reveal more fully the extent to which our weather in the lower layers is influenced by developments occurring aloft at impenetrable heights.

CHAPTER II

WHERE THE WEATHER IS BORN

IF we were able to estimate how much time the average person occupied in grumbling or rejoicing—more often the former—about the weather, we would possibly realise how greatly it affects our lives.

The true weather observer, however, whether he be a professional or amateur, finds this never-ending drama of nature, on a stage that never sets, a subject of the most absorbing study that grows ever more and more fascinating.

Most of us, of course, accept the different kinds of weather as they come round, but how many could explain where the weather comes from in the first place? It is probable that most of us would find considerable difficulty in answering such a question.

Obviously, the first step for the student of weather is to find the true answer to this all-important question, and in order to do so he must know something of the remarkable story of the atmosphere around us. He must learn what causes the weather to be continually changing its form and character without any apparently ordered plan, and why every day is not the same as every other, and all the years are not alike.

There is no standard design in this branch of nature to guide the researcher. There is no uniform pattern of behaviour that causes a great storm to develop suddenly out of an area of seeming calm; or any way of telling exactly what direction a storm may take, or at what rate it will travel. That is what makes long-range forecasting as chancy as spotting the Derby winner!

But we are able to trace how weather forms. The

7

atmosphere is composed of a number of gases, of which the most important is oxygen, for without it we could not live. This is a variable gas that decreases with altitude, which accounts for the fact that mountain climbers experience increasing effort and breathlessness as they ascend, and is the reason why pilots require an artificial supply when they fly at heights of about 20,000 feet and over.

The other variable gas in the atmosphere is water vapour, which is the source of all cloud and rain or snowfall, and is therefore of great importance to the weather researcher.

The lower layers of the atmosphere form a kind of reservoir for varying amounts of this water vapour. Water which has evaporated from the oceans is carried aloft by certain motions of the air and this condenses into rain or snow when it reaches a sufficient height. It is, therefore, within these layers of the atmosphere that all weather occurs.

Travelling continually through the atmosphere are huge masses of air which are more or less uniform in their composition, especially as regards temperatures and humidity. Most of these air masses cover an area of at least a quarter of a million square miles, and often much more than that.

The origin, development and movement of these air masses has to be studied by the weather men, as this information is necessary for plotting on the weather maps, known as synoptic charts. Each air mass acquires its particular physical character at its original source, and out of its subsequent behaviour come the eternal conflicts of the weather.

The largest sources of air masses are the polar and tropic regions. These masses come together over the vast Atlantic Ocean, and form an endless battle-ground where victory goes first to one and then to the other. (See Fig ii.)

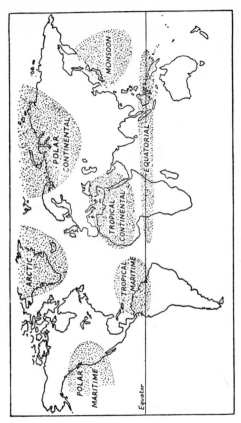

Fig. ii. Diagram of Main Air Masses

9

Each of these air masses brings a particular type of weather. It must be appreciated, however, that these weather conditions can be modified according to whether the air mass takes a long time in its travel, thus collecting new influences on its way. Nevertheless, each of the principal masses retains its main characteristic in spite of its long journeys and continuous battles.

The meteorologist has the job of tracking the probable course of the mass, from the time it leaves its original source region, and the rate at which it is likely to travel. Provided there are no major modifications *en route*, the type of weather in different parts of the world associated with each of these air masses is as follows:

(1) *Arctic and Polar Continental.* The source region is over Greenland, northern Russia, Finland and Spitzbergen. Owing to the dryness of this air mass, it usually brings fine, clear, sunny winter days to the British Isles and northern Europe. But if this air mass travels as far south as the Mediterranean, it will pick up modifications, become less dry and more unstable, and develop into a showery type of weather in southern Europe.

(2) *Polar Maritime.* Its source region is somewhere over the west coast of North America, and it carries generally fair weather, apart from occasional isolated thunder-storms.

(3) *Tropical Continental.* This travels in winter mainly over southern Europe, and from it develop most of the severe storms along the Mediterranean coasts.

(4) *Tropical Maritime.* Originating over the southern part of the North Atlantic Ocean, this is associated in summer with one of the best types of

fine weather development, referred to in our own weather forecasts as "an anticyclone over the Azores." It brings higher temperatures and more humidity than the other air masses, and for that reason will often produce sea fogs along the English Channel coast, while inland it will be brilliantly sunny. In winter, however, it frequently produces days of persistent drizzle and a muggy atmosphere.

(5) *Equatorial*. This operates mainly within the equatorial belt, and is confined to that recognised type of tropical weather.

(6) *Monsoon*. This air mass, which originates over southern Asia, draws hot, moisture-laden air from the Pacific Ocean. In summer it brings torrential rains to the vast area stretching from India to Korea. In winter the flow of winds is reversed, and the winds from the Pacific are deflected back into the Indian Ocean, and over the central land areas this maritime air mass meets tropical continental air, which is naturally dry.

(7) *Superior Air*. This high altitude air mass sometimes descends in midsummer over the high mountains and plateaux of the south-western states of North America. It is very dry and warm, originating as it does at about the top of the troposphere, and it retains these conditions so that by the time it reaches earth-level it is almost the hottest of any type of air.

It must be realised that, although the weather is born at such sources, it is modified and influenced not only by the passage of the air masses over the continents and the oceans, but also by topographical features on the earth's surface, such as mountains, valleys, lakes, forests, etc. These are important factors in determining climate, and are discussed in detail in the later chapter on the world's climates. Suffice it to say here that woodlands and forests increase annual rainfall; that large lakes, like oceans, have a tempering effect on coastal climates; that the days are normally cooler and the nights warmer on hilltops than in valleys; that wind velocity is reduced in large built-up areas and in dense forests.

Having traced the sources of the world's air masses, let us consider what happens to them in the development of weather. According to their behaviour and development, so are the special conditions built up that produce calm, fine weather areas, or high winds and storm centres.

The source region where an air mass has formed its main features, which are now affecting any particular area, is probably many hundreds of miles away. This proves that it is really the air masses that are the over-riding factor, and not the winds, as is so commonly believed. The varied characteristics of the winds are originally derived from the air masses, from the dreaded khamsin of the North African deserts to the bitter mistral of the French Alps.

It is necessary to realise at the outset that the deflecting force which pushes at all these winds is produced by the motion of the earth on its axis. As a result of this, to the observer on the ground the winds appear to travel along a curved path when they are really moving straight ahead.

Winds are created by the movement of air masses from areas of high pressure (fine weather) to areas of low pressure (rain). In a low-pressure area the increasing atmospheric suction causes the winds to travel around in a circle that is known as "cyclonic." In the northern hemisphere the motion is counter-clockwise and in the southern hemisphere it is clock-wise. On the extreme outward edge of the circular path the wind blows lightly, but increases more and more as it turns round the inward spiral towards the centre.

Within this cyclonic area the atmospheric pressure falls steadily and the barometer drops accordingly. The barometric pressure, therefore, is shown by a number of contour lines passing through a series of points on the particular part of the earth's surface.

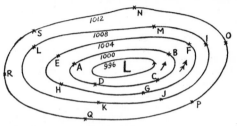

↑ ↑ *Wind Speed Code, shown by number of feathers on arrows*

Fig. iii. ISOBARS INDICATING A STORM AREA

These contour lines are depicted on a weather map in the same way as topographical contour lines are shown on an ordinary land ordnance map. The former are known as isobars, derived from the Greek word *iso*, meaning equal. The isobar on the weather map shows the points along which the height of the barometer is the same.

We notice on a land ordnance map how the centre of each contour circle is the apex of a hill or mountain. In the same way on the weather map the contour lines of isobars depict the apex of a high- or low-pressure system. The difference, however, is that whereas on a land map the contour lines are stationary, on a weather map they are always on the move

13

and only show the position of those contours at any given time. There is, therefore, a considerable fascination in tracing on, say, a weather map of the northern hemisphere all the different areas of storm and calm, rain clouds or clear skies.

We are also able to see from the development of these areas, at intervals of a few hours, how any particular storm centre is building up or decaying, in what direction it seems to be travelling, and what is the likelihood of its influence upon our own particular locality in the immediate future.

The speed of the wind is inversely proportionate to the distance between the isobars. For example, if the isobars are half an inch apart, the wind speed is double that of when the isobars are one inch apart, provided these are in the same latitude and the temperature is uniform.

Let us now have a look at a small corner of a weather map, and see what these isobars look like (Fig. iii). It will be noticed that round the centre of the storm area (996) the barometer reading is 1,000 millibars.* This isobar is drawn by finding that the reading of 1,000 millibars is reported from the weather stations A, B, C and D. These are accordingly linked up by the appropriate isobaric contour line. Stations E, F, G and H show readings a little higher, at 1,004 millibars, and so the next isobar line is drawn in the same way. The same procedure is, of course, followed for all the readings, until we have all our isobar lines complete, which shows how far afield the low-pressure area is extending.

The isobars shown on these weather maps appear

* One millibar is approximately the pressure exerted by a layer of water 1 centimetre deep. 1,000 millibars is the pressure of a column of mercury 29.531 inches long, at 0 degrees on the Centigrade scale of the barometer in latitude 45. Inches on the barometer can easily be converted into millibars as shown on the weather map, by the use of the tables in Appendix I.

14

as fairly regular continuous curved lines. Actually, they are not quite so regular as that, as there are obviously intruding fluctuations—even though slight —at the areas between the stations, where no observations are collected. They are not sufficient, however, to cause any inaccuracies in the general picture.

We now come to the next stage of plotting on the weather map the development of a depression, and here we are introduced to what is termed a "front." This is the boundary of two opposing air masses, shown on the weather map as a thick black line which signifies the position of the "front" on the earth.

When warm winds blow up from the south, and meet cold air from the opposite direction, these do not mix together as one might suppose. Each keeps its own individuality. When the south winds are gaining supremacy, and the cold air is in retreat, a "warm front" is produced. As the front approaches a particular locality, light rain begins to fall there, and this increases steadily in intensity until the "front" itself arrives. As the "front" passes away, the barometer begins to rise, the clouds break and quickly clear, and the sun shines out again.

When the north winds gain the upper hand, a "cold front" is formed. This produces a different type of weather from that of a "warm front," for whereas the latter gives us a period of fairly steady rain, the former brings sharp and often violent showers, interspersed with bright sunny intervals. In the summer, it is often associated with thunderstorms, and in the winter with hail or snow squalls.

It will be understood, therefore, that the formation of these "fronts" are stages in the life of a "depression" or rain area, and we can now follow, with the accompanying diagrams, the process by which a depression is built up.

The first thing that happens is that a slight kink develops along a stationary front, as seen in Fig. iv. Sometimes this will straighten out again, and no bad weather builds up, but more often it grows deeper and expands into a rain area that is called a trough. Such a development is shown in Fig. v (A, B and C).

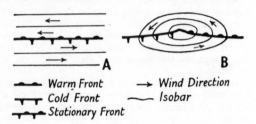

～～ Warm Front	→ Wind Direction
▬▬ Cold Front	～ Isobar
▬▲▬ Stationary Front	

Fig. iv. STATIONARY FRONT DEVELOPING INTO A RAIN "TROUGH"

As the trough grows deeper, the area of cloud and rain extends. Then something else begins to happen. The cold front starts to overtake the warm front, and then a third type of front develops, known as an Occluded Front.

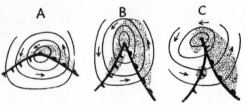

Fig. v. THREE STAGES IN THE DEVELOPMENT OF A DEPRESSION
(Shaded portion is the rain area)

The two fronts meet at an angle, resting over the earth's lower surface in the form of a "V," as shown in Fig. vi. It will be seen that there are now three distinct air masses; a warm air mass above the front, a cold air mass pushing at the left flank of the cold front, and a cool air mass immediately ahead of the warm front.

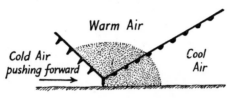

Fig. vi. THE TWO FRONTS

This is the beginning of the final stage when the cold front starts to lift the warm front, and the shape changes from a "V" to a "Y" (Fig. vii). The rain area subsides, and the central area of low pressure begins to fill up, until the contour lines (isobars) on the weather map straighten out again, and a period of calm, quiet weather returns for a while.

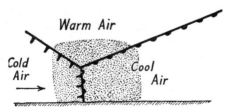

Fig. vii. BEGINNING OF THE FINAL STAGE OF A DEPRESSION

We can now begin to realise that a weather map is not just a deadly dull chart of statistics, but a picture showing the violent upheavals or the still, gentle conditions of the weather over the different localities. The isobars are no longer plain lines on a map, but fire the imagination as they curve and plunge to depict the areas of storm and calm.

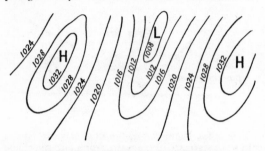

Fig. viii. A TROUGH OF LOW PRESSURE

Let us, therefore, conclude this chapter by summarising the pictures that the isobars draw.

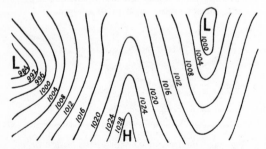

Fig. ix. A RIDGE OF HIGH PRESSURE

A high-pressure area, where the barometer is high and the weather mainly fine, is called a *High*, and is shown on the weather map by the letter H in a closed isobar. This is also known as an *Anticyclone*. A low-pressure area, where the barometer is low and the weather unsettled and stormy, is called a *Low*, and is shown on the map by the letter L in a closed isobar (Fig. iii). This is also known as a *Depression*. An area of low pressure between two "Highs" is called a *Trough*, and is in fact in the shape of a trough or valley on the map (Fig. viii). An area of high pressure between two "Lows" is called a *Ridge*, and looks very much like a mountain ridge on the map (Fig. ix).

CHAPTER III

THE WINDS AND THEIR CURRENTS

RIGHT back to biblical times, winds have been a source of interest and conjecture, and have—according to the points of the compass from which they blow—been associated with certain types of weather.

This relationship, however, is not so simple as most people have been led to believe. We can have quite a variety of weather with wind from the same quarter. We can have sunny skies or driving rain on a southerly wind; we can have drought or a period of continuous rain on a north-easterly wind; we can have severe cold or extreme heat on an easterly wind.

The weather does not depend so much on the quarter from which the wind is blowing, as from its source region that we discussed in the previous chapter when talking of air masses. This proves that it is not the wind direction that matters so much as the source of the air mass itself.

In studying the behaviour of the winds, we must first realise that this planet on which we live is continually spinning from west to east, pulling the atmosphere with it. Westerly winds incline to develop in the upper atmosphere, but as they move faster than the earth is spinning, they are thrown outwards from the earth's axis. This means that they are thrown southwards, and a mass of air is piled up towards the south that builds up a high-pressure system there, and produces a correspondingly low-pressure system to the north.

In the winter, this high-pressure area will be found farther south than in the summer, and is usually lying over the Azores and stretching across to Bermuda. In the summer (especially when we have a good one) it moves north and at intervals will stretch right across the British Isles and give us two or three weeks of real summer weather.

These pressure systems are the basis of the great winds of the world, the two most important being the *Trades* and the *Westerlies*. The former are so named because they keep to a definite track (derived from the old German word *trede*).

The Trade Winds blow in the areas between about 30° and 10° N. and S. latitudes, and their mean direction is from north-east in the northern hemisphere and south-east in the southern. They are much more constant and regular than the Westerlies, so that it is possible to know approximately what winds are to be found on any day. Air that descends from the higher levels in the sub-tropical high-pressure areas is largely responsible for feeding these winds.

The reason why the Westerlies are so much more variable is because they are due to a very complex system of irregular pressure areas. Their main tracks are to the north and south of the calm regions, and they blow with greater regularity in the southern seas than in the northern hemisphere where they are deflected by land masses and other weather factors. They blow hardest in the region between 40° S. and 50° S. latitude, which you will often hear spoken of as the "Roaring Forties."

The constancy of the Trade Winds is stressed right through the world's history. They enabled Columbus, for instance, to journey time after time to the Caribbean Islands with amazing accuracy, although he was an untrained navigator.

The Trade Winds come together in a belt of calms known as the *Doldrums*, which we hear about so often in tales of the sea, where sailing ships can get caught and lay motionless for days or even weeks.

There are a number of winds that are peculiar to different parts of the world, and should rightly be termed "local" winds. Let us visit some of these regions.

Over the wide desert areas of the Middle East there is a wind called the *Harmattan*, which sometimes carries the fine dust of the Sahara as far as 100 miles out to sea, and will cause quite a thick fog. This is very different from the harmless type of sea fog off our British coasts; it is, in fact, a most distressing fog of dust particles that fills up your eyes and lungs, and even penetrates the pores of the skin.

In the Sudan is a wind known as the *Haboob* (which is the Arabic word for "wind"), and this takes the form of a spiral motion, which can whirl the dust at times up to heights of over 5,000 feet. The dust will get into everything, and if motor-cars or aircraft are caught, the engines will become completely choked in a few minutes. These are not violent winds, however, and seldom exceed 30 miles an hour, except in gusts.

No rain is associated with these winds, but observers have reported that the squalls seem to approach with a peculiar rustling sound, out of an air that immediately before has been perfectly calm. They are usually experienced between May and September and average about twenty a year.

The *Sirocco* is another desert wind, that blows along the south and east Mediterranean, being drawn mainly from the great Arabian and North African deserts. It is a very hot, dry, dust-laden wind. The same wind which blows in Egypt is there known as the *Khamsin*.

In the opposite direction are the cold winds, of which the most noted is the *Mistral*, that blows through the Rhône valley. It is drawn directly from the French Alps, and is bitterly cold, and often of hurricane force.

A similar wind is the *Bora*, that is a feature of the Adriatic Sea, and has its source in the same region as the Mistral. These two winds are not accompanied by any rain-storms, and will often roar with full violence throughout brilliant sunny, cloudless days.

Another Alpine wind is the famous *Föhn*, usually confined to the deeper, more enclosed Alpine valleys. This, however, is not one of the cold winds, but often carries a very trying, excessively dry heat. It will blow for several days on end.

Passing now across to Australia, we find a wind which is well known in that continent, and goes by the strange name of *Willy Willy*. This is a wind of tornado violence, that is accompanied by torrential rain, and often causes widespread damage to any buildings in its path.

A wind that has a peculiar feature is the *Southerly Buster* of New South Wales. Although it is a cold wind, it is always preceded by a hot northerly wind, called the *Brickfielder*.

In South Africa there is a hot wind that goes by the name of the *Berg*. It brings the heat from the high plateau over which it passes, down to the lower levels. It naturally brings a good deal of personal discomfort, but at the same time it has some practical value, because it speeds up the ripening of fruit in the valleys in autumn. A similar kind of wind is the *Chinook*, in Colorado and Alberta.

The British Isles is free of any of these peculiar winds, and all that we experience are variations in direction and strength. Our prevailing wind is from the west, as most of our weather travels from the west towards the east. That is to say, the "depressions" (bad weather areas) and the anticyclones (fine weather areas) mostly reach us from over the Atlantic.

Here you have the basis for the old saying that a "veering" wind brings fair weather, and a "backing" wind brings foul weather. We have learnt in the previous chapter that the wind blows clockwise round the high-pressure systems and anti-clockwise round the low ones. From this you will see that the wind must back (i.e. shift *against* the sun) as a low advances, and must veer (i.e. shift *with* the sun) as the low passes away to the east and the high advances from the west.

This makes it possible for you to find out where the bad weather area is lying. If you stand with your back to the wind (in the northern hemisphere), the low-pressure area—and consequently the bad weather—will be on your left-hand side. (In the southern hemisphere the reverse holds good.) This rule was laid down by a Dutch professor named Buys Ballot in 1857, as a result of close study of the weather charts, and ever since then it has been known as Buys Ballot's Rule.

So far we have been mainly concerned with wind direction, and its circulation systems, but we also have to study its force. Sir Francis Beaufort, an admiral of the British Navy, drew up a scale to denote the speed of wind, giving each range of speed a number that corresponded to the amount of sail a man-of-war could carry in such a wind. This came to be established as the official wind scale, and it is still used today, and is known as the Beaufort Wind Scale.

This scale is used only for surface observation, and is the speed of the wind up to 30 feet above the ground. Looking at the scale on the next page, it will be seen that a whole gale is Force 10, and it is very rare to experience anything more severe than

24

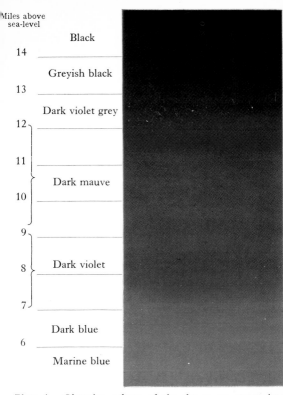

Miles above
sea-level

Black

14

Greyish black

13

Dark violet grey

12

11

Dark mauve

10

9

Dark violet

8

7

Dark blue

6

Marine blue

Plate 1. *Changing colours of the sky at an ascent into higher altitudes.*

F.P. 24

Plate 2. *"Fairweather" cumulus clouds breaking up at sunset.*

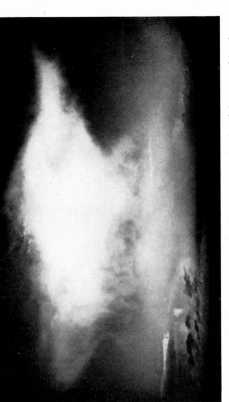

Plate 3.   A cloud of the cumulus family, known as the Anvil, because of its shape.

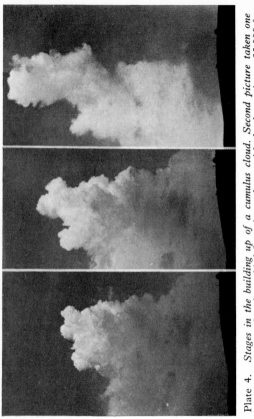

Plate 4. *Stages in the building up of a cumulus cloud. Second picture taken one minute after first; third five minutes later, with cloud towering to 35,000 ft.*

Plate 5. *The shower cumulus cloud building up in front of an advancing squall.*

Plate 6. *Cumulonimbus cloud seen rising up from a long base line, building up for a storm.*

Plate 7. *A typical altocumulus cloud.*

Plate 8. *In the top picture the red flush extends too far over the sky to promise a fine morrow. In the lower picture, the even red sunset glow is indicative of fine weather.*

Plate 9.   The altocumulus cloud of a type that forms in large globular masses.

Plate 10. *Stratocumulus clouds spreading across the sky in billows and more popularly known as "roller" clouds.*

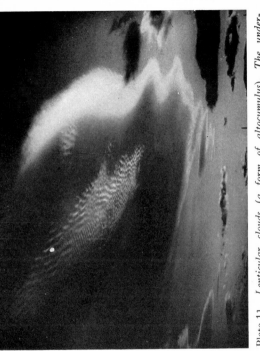

Plate 11. *Lenticular clouds (a form of altocumulus). The under-surfaces have a delicately rippled structure.*

Plate 12. *Two good examples of a fine sunset, with the red glow along the horizon.*

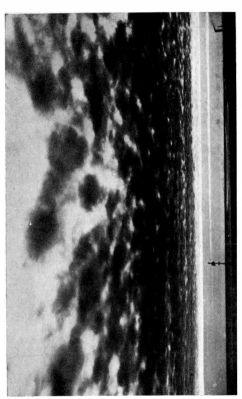

Plate 13. *Stratocumulus clouds forming in lines towards the horizon, and producing a wavy appearance.*

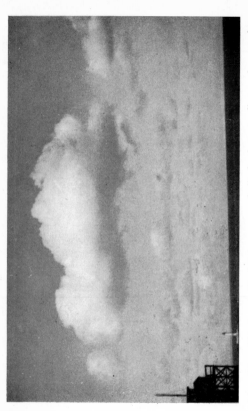

Plate 14. *This is a typical "shower-cumulus" cloud, portending a showery day with sunny intervals.*

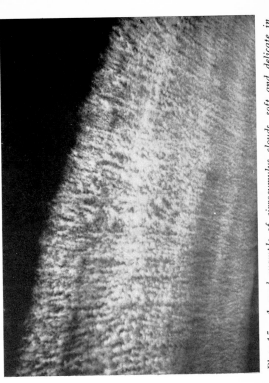

Plate 15. *A good example of cirrocumulus clouds, soft and delicate in outline.*

Plate 16. *The cirrus cloud forming in bands at two levels.*

that in Great Britain, except in gusts. When we realise, therefore, that a whole gale does not produce a constant wind of more than 63 miles an hour, we may imagine the terrific damage and loss of life that can be caused in those countries that experience hurricanes and tornadoes, where the wind rises to as much as 150 miles an hour, tearing a narrow passage through main streets of a city, bringing down whole buildings, and even overturning cars and trains. This would be three times the velocity of what we know as a "strong gale."

THE BEAUFORT SCALE OF WIND FORCE

Beaufort Number	Description of Wind	Limits of Velocity	Effects on Land
0	Calm	less than 1	Smoke rises vertically.
1	Light Air	1–3	Direction shown by smoke, but not by wind-vanes.
2	Light Breeze	4–7	Wind felt on face; leaves rustle; ordinary vane moved by wind.
3	Gentle Breeze	8–12	Leaves and small twigs in constant motion; wind extends light flag.
4	Moderate Breeze	13–18	Raises dust and loose paper; small branches are moved.
5	Fresh Breeze	19–24	Small trees in leaf begin to sway.
6	Strong Breeze	25–31	Large branches in motion; umbrellas used with difficulty.
7	Moderate Gale	32–38	Whole trees in motion: inconvenience felt when walking against wind.
8	Fresh Gale	39–46	Breaks twigs off trees; generally impedes progress.
9	Strong Gale	47–54	Slight structural damage; chimney-pots and slates removed.
10	Whole Gale	55–63	Trees uprooted; considerable structural damage.
11	Storm	64–75	Widespread damage; very rarely experienced.
12	Hurricane	Above 75	Countryside is devastated.

Generally, winter winds are of a higher velocity than summer ones, the reason for this being that barometric pressure varies more gradually in summer than winter. Also, nights are normally calmer than days, except in stormy periods. In fine weather you will often notice that the early morning is dead calm, with hardly a leaf stirring, but by early afternoon there may be quite a moderate breeze blowing. This is because daytime heating causes a mixing of the upper and lower layers of air, and this in turn brings down to the surface some of the more swiftly moving air from above.

Most of us know that there is generally more wind at the coasts than inland. But have we studied the reason for this? It is understandable that when the sun is shining the land temperature will rise much more quickly than the sea temperature. At the end of the day, the source of warmth is withdrawn, and the land gives up its heat more quickly than the water. This unequal heating and cooling of land and water causes air currents to sweep in from the sea, and a sea breeze is felt on shore and a short way inland (but not far). The wind quickly loses its velocity as it passes from sea to land.

We are apt to think of wind as having a cooling effect, but this is not always the case. It depends very much on the air temperature. At a low, or even average temperature, if the wind is blowing at more than 15 miles an hour, our bodies are cooled considerably. But if the temperature is high—over 80° F. in the shade, for instance—a strong wind will have the opposite effect. It will add to the heating of our bodies. The reason for this is that the wind, blowing through this high temperature, has then become too hot to offset the normal cooling that we would otherwise get from increased evaporation.

There is one further point to understand about

the wind, and that is its inconstant force. It never blows steadily at a given number of miles an hour, but travels along in a series of gusts. The gustiness is greater during gales, and also more marked on land than at sea. So when you read in the paper that the wind reached 70 miles an hour at some place on the coast, it means that some of the gusts reached that speed for not more than a minute at a time, whereas the mean wind force was probably not more than about 45 or 50 miles.

CHAPTER IV

THE STORY OF THE CLOUDS

THE clouds passing daily across our skies are such a
familiar sight that we rarely give a thought as to
where they come from and what causes them. Their
formation is due to condensation of the atmosphere
taking place at higher levels. A certain amount of
water vapour is to be found in our lower atmosphere and its amount is in proportion to the temperature of the air. The higher the temperature the
greater the amount. When warm air is cooled there
comes a point when condensation must take place,
because there is a limit to the amount of water
vapour existing in any volume for each degree of
temperature. It is this temperature which is termed
"dewpoint." A cloud can be formed only when the
air is cooled below its "dewpoint."

Different types of cloud are formed by different
atmospheric conditions. There are three main types:
cirrus, cumulus and stratus, from which develop
many intermediate gradations that are often a combination of two or more individual cloud formations.

Cirrus clouds form the highest layer of the cloud
family, and sometimes stretch right up to the lower
level of the stratosphere. These clouds are composed
of frozen vapour particles which we often speak of
as "mares' tails." They have the least density of any
and the greatest variety of formation. In appearance
they are fibrous, and stretch in thin streaks across the
sky in all directions when a change in the weather
is approaching.

The fibres extend horizontally or vertically. If
they develop into sheets and fall rapidly in altitude,

and then assume a formation somewhat resembling shoals of fishes, rainy weather is imminent. The wind will veer in the direction in which the streaks of cirrus run across the sky. Also, if these fibres appear to be brushed backwards at one end, and the direction is opposite to that of the prevailing wind, it will eventually change direction accordingly. If that direction be south-east or south-west, heavy rain and high winds will follow.

Furthermore, if the fibres are pointing *upwards*, it means that the clouds are descending and rain is approaching, but if they point *downwards* the converse holds good.

The next in the cloud family is the *Cumulus*, the most familiar cloud of all, which is associated with both fine and showery weather, according to whether it is "fair-weather" or "shower" cumulus. You will see the former as banks of soft white clouds drifting leisurely across the sky on a summer's day and melting away at sunset. The "shower" cumulus, however, rises like gigantic puffs of smoke from a long base-line, and sometimes may reach up to 1½ miles high. These clouds, unlike the "fair-weather" cumulus, are inclined to increase in density towards sunset, till they gradually cover the greater part of the sky.

These billowing and towering clouds take their name from the same Latin derivation from which comes the word "accumulate."

The third branch of the cloud family is the *Stratus*, which is the lowest type of all clouds and will sometimes descend to within a few hundred feet of ground-level. When these clouds form at the top of a hill they are usually a forerunner of rain. The atmosphere below a sheet of stratus is frequently very clear and distant objects like ships at sea 10 or 12 miles away look quite near at hand.

This type of cloud consists of an even, continuous layer all the way through, and sometimes looks very much like a high bank of fog.

We now come to the subdivisions of these main groups.

There are two distinct members of the cirrus family. The *Cirrostratus* is the lowest type of cirrus cloud and even that may be as much as 4 to 5 miles high. This is the type of sky that gives a watery appearance to the sun or moon and a milky look generally. It also causes those rings or haloes around the sun or moon that forecast approaching rain.

Cirrocumulus cloud might be described as the last mentioned cloud's sister. It sometimes appears as faint ripples like those on wind-blown sand, and is more commonly spoken of as a "mackerel" sky. When you see these small, dappled clouds in groups high in the sky, during a fine spell, you may be sure there is a change for the worse coming, but there is one consolation. It will herald one of those typically unsettled days that is not very wet for long, even though it may not be very fine for long, either.

These clouds often provide beautiful sunsets when they take on a deeper and deeper grand red hue in the setting sun.

The *Cumulus* family is the largest group, of which there are four members.

Cumulonimbus is the familiar rain cloud. It is caused by varying degrees of atmosphere and rain-type clouds which aircraft pilots try to avoid as they often experience severe icing conditions when flying through them. Occasionally a cumulonimbus cloud will reverse its normal position and converge *towards* the earth or sea in pyramid form. When that happens it will sometimes produce a miniature cyclone over a narrow strip of land or a water-spout at sea.

30

Altocumulus cloud can be distinguished from the last-mentioned type because it appears in larger globular masses. Sometimes these masses spread out, looking like small waves, but often they are closely packed together in dense groups. At other times they may be seen in bands over the sun towards the horizon and this is not a good weather sign at sunset.

Castellatus is a type of cumulus that assumes the shape of castles or turrets. These are more often to be seen in the summer months and are individual cloudlets of middle height.

Mammatocumulus appears as tiny clouds on the lower surface of a cumulus layer, suspended like folds of drapery hung in festoons. (It is sometimes called a "festoon" cloud.) It indicates very stormy weather, with wind and torrential rain (or snow in winter), sometimes accompanied by thunder.

If you live in the south of England, especially along the Channel coast, you will have heard people talking about "Folkestone pillars." They are a series of towering conical cloud-banks rising up from a dense base, frequently seen during showery weather with sunny intervals, and are another of the cumulus cloud family.

Yet another type of the cumulus family is the scud cloud. This is a low mass of thin cloud that seems to fly at a great rate across the sky—sometimes throughout the whole day—and clear away completely at sunset, without bringing any rain.

In April you may notice a cloud that forms the shape of an anvil, and is popularly known as the anvil cloud. It is really a cross between a cumulus and stratus, and is associated with showery weather —those sudden bursts of rain or hail, with brilliantly sunny intervals.

The *Stratus* family has three members.

Stratocumulus can usually be defined by its appearance as a layer or patches of globular cloud masses. These are very regularly arranged, the smallest of them being fairly large, and are mostly soft and grey, with some darker parts. Sometimes they arrange themselves in lines towards the horizon. Very often the rolls are so close that their edges join together; when they cover the sky, as is often the case in winter, they have a wavy appearance. A somewhat uncommon variation of this cloud is known as the "roller" cloud when it spreads across the sky in billows.

Nimbostratus is a typical rain cloud. This layer of cloud at a low altitude is in the main of a dark grey colour and nearly uniform. It is the type of cloud which on many occasions brings continuous rain or snow. Sometimes this cloud will break up into shreds in a high wind, and then becomes known as *Fractonimbus*. Its formation should be carefully watched. If some high, thin clouds form above it as it approaches, shooting out in different directions, and very numerous, then the rain will be heavy and lasting. If, however, there are only very few of these upper shoots of cloud, then the rain will be less heavy and soon over.

The rearguard of a nimbus is sometimes called a "Rag Cloud," owing to its ugly ragged-looking appearance, as it rolls along behind the rain-storm, accompanied by a high wind. It usually grows smaller in such cases, which means that the weather is about to clear up again, but if you should notice it is increasing, then look out for a bad gale.

In the same way that nimbostratus is the lowest type of stratus cloud, so is *Altostratus* the highest cloud of this family. It is another of those skies that look very milky in appearance, and gives that watery effect to the sun or moon.

Apart from the fact that the study of clouds is a fascinating hobby to the amateur observer, it is also of great importance to the aviator, who is concerned so much with their composition, speed, developments, and so on. Clouds also have a very definite bearing on coming weather, according to their particular behaviour.

Speed is one of the things to watch. When you see clouds moving leisurely across the sky, fair weather is likely to continue, but if they begin to scud across rapidly, then look out for wind and rain.

Formation is another matter. If the small clouds of late afternoon decrease and melt away towards sunset, fair weather is assured, but if they increase to cover the greater part of the sky, then you may expect unsettled weather on the morrow. If the clouds during the daytime have delicate edges merging softly into the blue background of the sky, this is a fine-weather sign, but if they have sharply defined edges that stand out against the blue, stormy weather is imminent.

Height is also a thing to watch. Near the end of a fine spell, clouds will sometimes begin to form very high in the sky. In that case, the change from fine to rainy weather will be gradual, perhaps a couple of days ahead. But there is one point about gradual changes, and that is that when the weather breaks it is a more prolonged spell.

The last point to watch is direction. If the higher clouds are moving in a different direction to that of the prevailing wind below, or of the lower clouds, it means that a general change of wind, to the direction of the higher clouds, is approaching. When there is a frosty spell being experienced, and the higher clouds change from north-east to south-west, then you may be sure that a thaw is near.

Although we get the drier weather from the eastern point of the compass, and the rainy weather from the west, it is a very bad outlook if rain *does* start when the wind is in the east, for it nearly always continues for at least 12 hours and sometimes 24 hours.

The worst time for rain to set in is about 9 o'clock in the morning, for this often heralds a wet day. Another unwelcome hour is about 2 p.m., for rain starting then is usually the forerunner of a wet afternoon. This, of course, does not apply to weather of a showery type, which can bring rain at any hour of the day.

As an amateur observer—even from my schooldays—I have found it a useful idea to tabulate at the end of each day what type of sunset, and what cloud changes of importance during the day, have been noted, and then in the opposite column enter details of the following day's weather. This gives you a very good check on the accuracy of your local skies for forecasting purposes, and also teaches a great deal of sky and cloud lore.

In making these observations, it is also useful to combine the various points that have already been mentioned with the sky hues, as there are certain colours in the sky that are associated with particular types of weather.

Yellow is one of the worst colours, especially at sunset, and is most feared by fishermen and all whose duties are on the seas. It is a colour that is always a forerunner of storm, heavy gales and rain. It does not always follow on the next day, but often is a warning for about 36 hours ahead.

Red can be a very misleading colour, as it is associated with both fine and foul weather. A red glow over the western sky at sunset, evenly diffused, means a fine morrow, and the same holds good if the red is in long narrow streaks of high cloud drawn across the setting sun. But if the red is reflected on lowering masses of ragged cloud, especially if the glow spreads right across the sky towards the east, then very stormy weather may be expected. Red is also a bad sign in the eastern sky at dawn.

You will often notice, in showery weather, that the sky is green in the clear places between the clouds, instead of the more familiar blue. This means that the upper atmosphere is very moist, and signifies a continuance of showery weather interspersed with sunny intervals.

We usually think of a blue sky as being associated with fine weather, but this is not always so. It all depends on the shade of blue. A very dark blue sky against which the clouds are sharply outlined is a forerunner of stormy weather, but a soft, light blue means settled weather.

We all know that bright copper tints around cloud edges are a sign of electric disturbances in the atmosphere, and bring thunder-storms.

Sometimes you will see puffy clouds strongly tinted with violet, usually brought on a spell of easterly winds. This is a colour generally confined to the winter months, and is experienced when we have days of cold, cloudy weather, but without rain.

Grey skies are usually rain skies, particularly when a blue sky gradually changes to a consistent ashy grey that spreads over the whole area. You must be careful, however, not to confuse this with the yellowish-grey gloom that approaches from the east during periods of drought, and is quite often mistaken for a gathering storm.

A study of sky colours will be of considerable interest and practical value to the weather observer, but the reason for these colours should also be understood.

The best example is to take that of colours passing through a prism. When rays of sunlight pass through the atmosphere—particularly if it is laden with moisture—they are broken up into their component colours in the same manner as when they pass through a prism.

The main colours that we see in different parts of the sky depend on the amount of this breaking up—or "scattering"—of the rays, which in its turn is affected by the number and size of the particles of moisture in the atmosphere.

On a fine day, these particles are normally few and small, so we generally have a blue sky. If the atmosphere grows moister, these particles increase in number and size, so that the shorter wave-length blue rays are turned aside, and the long-wave reds and yellows begin to predominate.

It will, therefore, be understood that there is a scientific reason for the association of certain sky colours with approaching weather, and that they are not based merely on familiar "weather saws."

CHAPTER V

WHEN IT RAINS

WHAT makes it rain? This is a question to which even weather experts find it difficult to give a simple straightforward answer. There is a great deal continually going on in the upper air which has yet to be discovered, but we do know that rainfall depends on the amount of instability in the upper air.

At this stage we have to understand what is meant by instability. A mass of unsaturated air becomes unstable when the rate of change of temperature with height exceeds 5·4° F. in every 1,000 feet. When it does this it exceeds the cooling rate of the mass of air rising through the atmosphere, which means that the ascending air will be warmer and therefore lighter than the other air around it, and so it rises just like a cork in water.

It has been proved that large areas of rainfall are associated with these upper air temperature differences. Very often rain will then fall, even though the barometer is remaining high and steady.

Rainfall is affected by local features such as hills or a coast-line, and it is generally greater at high altitudes. This is because the air comes into contact with the cold surfaces of these higher regions, so that the previously warm air becomes cool as it is forced up the hills or mountains. But there is no definite scale of a given rate of rainfall increase with feet above sea-level, because so many other local factors may affect the matter.

Hills—and mountains even more so—therefore have a considerable effect on the weather by influencing the amount of rainfall and often changing the flow of air currents. It will thus be realised that valleys may have an entirely different climate from the hills and mountains above them. In our own country good examples are Snowdonia, the English Lake district and the Highlands of Scotland. The mountain areas are much rainier and cooler by day, though often warmer at night. In the Highlands of Scotland on the western (windward) slopes the mean annual rainfall is more than 170 inches, while on the leeward side around Moray Firth it is no more than 25 inches.

Over land areas rainfall is greater than over the sea. Water is slower to warm up and slower to cool down over large stretches of ocean, and so there are not such extremes of temperature.

How far this tempering influence spreads inland depends partly on the prevailing wind direction and partly on the relative area of land in proportion to sea.

For example, in the British Isles the sea influence affects the whole country to a greater or lesser degree, as the prevailing winds are south-west—bringing the moist, mild air from the Atlantic—and the distance across Britain is small in comparison with that of the continent of Europe. Naturally, the western coasts receive the maximum moderating influence, and the Midlands the minimum; but the climate is definitely more temperate than it would be if Britain were joined on to the main continent.

The annual rainfall decreases as we proceed eastwards across Europe. We know that the Atlantic Ocean is the source of most atmospheric moisture and we can therefore expect the highest rainfall to be in Ireland and the lowest on the east coast of Britain.

In the same way that large areas of sea affect the inland climates, so do the different ocean currents.

In the temperate zones the ocean currents circulate from west to east, and the reverse is the case in the tropical zones. Warm currents increase the rainfall while cold currents decrease it. The reason for this is that the air which flows over warm ocean currents naturally becomes saturated at a comparatively high temperature, while air flowing over cold ocean currents becomes warmer and drier on contacting land.

To a somewhat lesser extent the larger lakes of the world influence the surrounding land climates. Places on the borders of these lakes have a slightly more temperate climate and a smaller rainfall than those farther inland.

Annual rainfall is also greater in forest and wooded areas. That is why afforestation schemes are sometimes put into operation to lessen the effects of drought areas.

Plateaux are conducive to high rainfalls, and one of the most notable in Britain is Princetown, on Dartmoor, which is 1,359 feet above sea-level and has more than double the rainfall of other places not many miles away, that are nearer to sea-level. Exmoor is another similar example, although it does not experience quite such a high rainfall as Dartmoor.

The rainiest spot in England is in Borrowdale, Cumberland, where the annual fall is 165 inches, as compared to some places on the east coast which have less than 20 inches a year.

A good deal of care should be exercised when reading in the newspapers or reference books that the month's rainfall has been so many inches. This can be very misleading, because one heavy thunderstorm may record more rainfall than a week or two of light rain. You will see, therefore, that it could so happen that the place which had, say, 2 inches of rainfall in the month might have had about twenty-nine fine days with the whole of the rainfall having been experienced in one heavy storm on a single day. Another place with, say, only 1½ inches of rainfall in the month may have had more than half the month consisting of wet days with the rain spread fairly evenly over the period.

The most accurate guide for the observer, therefore, for checking whether the particular month has been wet or fine, is to tabulate the *number of days* with rain.

Annual reports are usually given in decimal parts of an inch; 0·1 inch (namely, one-tenth) means an equivalent of about 10 tons to the acre, which equals 2,262 gallons.

Those who believe in the law of averages will find interest in the rainfall statistics of the British Isles, from which it is possible to deduce which are the most rainless periods throughout the year.

Sir Napier Shaw, the famous meteorologist, computed from "rain day" statistics (as opposed to rainfall ones) that the chances of using an umbrella on the average for the whole year in this country are 1 in 10, with individual months as follows:

October: 1 in 8. February: 1 in 9. June: 1 in 12.

Although we naturally grumble about rain coming in holiday periods, the farmer and gardener rejoice to see it after a period of fine, dry weather.

Probably we do not give much thought to the size of raindrops, but these vary according to different conditions inside the clouds and in the surrounding atmosphere. The usual type of rain consists of fairly fine drops, and these measure only 0·01 inch in diameter. The heavier type of rainfall may have drops just over 0·1 inch, and the largest drops such as we get during a thunder-storm average about twice this. Very often the larger drops that form will break up into smaller drops almost as soon as they leave the cloud.

Another point worth considering is at what speed rain falls from the clouds to the ground. As might be expected, the larger raindrops come down with more force than the smaller ones, but their speed is checked by the resistance of the air. When this resistance is equal to the weight of the drops the speed of fall is reduced, and then becomes constant, and this constant speed is known as the "terminal velocity." This rate is approximately:

Fine drops	2 miles an hour
Medium drops	15 miles an hour
Large drops	18 miles an hour

Let us now follow the life of an ordinary raindrop to see when and how it sometimes turns into a hailstone. The first stage is when a little water condenses on a tiny particle in the air. This next meets other particles and consequently grows in size. But it does not naturally fall straight to earth. There is often a strong enough ascending current of air to carry the raindrop aloft and it will not fall to earth until it grows large enough to descend through the updraught.

When these raindrops are carried in such an updraught to a level at which the temperature is very low, they will freeze and fall to earth in the form of hailstones. This most usually happens during summer thunder-storms when the conditions are such as to produce violent updraughts in the atmosphere.

Have you ever examined a hailstone carefully? If so, you will find that some of the larger ones look rather like onions with quite a number of skins or layers of hard clear ice alternating with soft opaque ice. There is a reason for these layers. When the raindrop reaches the top of the updraught and freezes into a hailstone this is thrown out and begins to fall to earth. But in a violent thunder-storm the updraught is being continually reinforced, which means that the hailstones have their descent halted and are shot upwards again when they form a further layer of ice. This is sometimes repeated over and over again and hailstones with more than twenty layers of ice have been found occasionally.

The size and weight of hailstones varies very much. In the British Isles it is rare to find any weighing more than about 10 ounces, but hailstones of that size have been reported from storms in the London area and elsewhere. In America, where Nature seems to do things on a grander scale, hailstones the size of tennis balls, and occasionally grapefruit, have been reported, sufficiently heavy to kill anyone whom they strike. One of the severest storms reported was on 6th July, 1928, in Nebraska, where hailstones were gathered, weighed and measured on standard store scales, and one stone was found to be 17 inches in circumference and weighing $1\frac{1}{2}$ lb.

One of the heaviest hail-storms reported in Britain, in relation to the size of hailstones, occurred in southern England on 1st July 1968; in several areas hailstones the size of golf balls fell and in Cardiff a hailstone that was measured proved to be the same size as a tennis ball.

From the formation of hailstones we pass to that of snow crystals. Snow-flakes form when water vapour condenses at a temperature below freezing-point, namely, $32°F$. But the mystery of snow-crystals is that no two are ever alike; when one considers the millions of crystals that fall in a snow-storm, this is an amazing feat of Nature. It has formed the basis of many scientific papers both in this country and America, and the variety of designs that the numerous photographs depict is remarkable.

Every one of these beautiful snow-crystals is six-sided and the simple shapes that form seem to grow by magic into more elaborate designs. When the weather is very cold the snow will fall in separate dry powdery crystals which can be taken and carefully examined. Many of the snow-crystals, of course, form in the upper air without descending as snow, because they will melt on the way down unless the surface temperature is at or near freezing-point. You must not confuse a snow-flake with a snow-crystal, as a flake is made up of a large number of crystals. One flake, in fact, may sometimes comprise two to three dozen crystals.

Snowfalls have two opposite results; they can create confusion and difficulty, or give much benefit. We all know the chaos that they can cause to road or rail transport, but in the other direction snow provides a very valuable blanket over the land and protects growing seeds and vegetation from extreme cold. Without the snow blanket many of the plants would be killed. Snow is a poor conductor of heat and therefore keeps the warmth in and the cold out; this also explains why we often hear of sheep being buried in deep snow-drifts and rescued alive after several days. Although the bottom of a snow layer can be so warm, the top surface is extremely cold, particularly on clear nights; even on a clear sunny winter's day, snow-covered ground will keep the air temperature lower than if the ground were free of snow. There has been recorded a difference of as much as 50 degrees between the top and bottom of a snow blanket.

In the British Isles snow is more frequent during the latter part of the winter and early spring, and this is because there is a greater tendency for easterly winds from the Continent to bring in the coldest weather around February and March.

Severe snow-storms can often be very local. We have had examples in southern England, with blizzards depositing a foot or more of snow in, say, one part of Kent, and places a few miles away without any snow at all. The explanation for this is that the heaviest falls occur along the continental side of a "warm front," which in this country, of course, is the south-eastern side. The snow rapidly decreases in amount on the opposite side of the front.

We often hear it said that it is "too cold for snow." Actually, it can never be *too* cold to snow, but when the temperature falls low in the British Isles it is generally during an anticyclone, or fine weather spell, and with the oncoming depression the temperature rises.

When snow becomes compressed over a long period of extreme freezing it congeals into ice and forms ice-streams known as glaciers. These glaciers move down the valleys from the mountains, and as they grow and pressure increases they gain such force as to tear up rocks from their beds and carry them forward on the stream.

As we know, the summits of many mountains are covered with snow all the year round. The snow line, however, varies in different parts of the world and according to the weather conditions of a particular year. This snow line is normally as low as about 8,000 feet in the Alps, but on the equator it is as high as about 16,000 feet. The level of the snow line is affected by prevailing winds in much the same way as we have seen that rainfall is influenced. The snow line is lower in mountain districts that are rainy than in any of those in the drier regions.

When rain and snow mix and fall together they produce sleet. This is caused by a layer of warm air

44

between the surface of the earth and the clouds, and as the snow passes through this layer it partly melts. Sometimes, however, it will freeze again as it reaches the ground, and create a very dangerous thin layer of ice.

Although snow is associated with Christmas in the northern hemisphere and is a regular feature of Christmas cards and stories, weather statistics prove that snow rarely falls in Christmas week. The Greenwich records show that, over a period of 83 years, snow has fallen on Christmas Day on only six occasions, and on Boxing Day on twelve occasions. Only twice has it snowed on Christmas Eve. These figures apply to southern England only, but even in the Midlands and the north of England it is more usual to have a "green" than a "white" Christmas.

CHAPTER VI

STORM AND TEMPEST

ONE of the grandest skyscapes to the observer is undoubtedly the building-up process of a thunder-cloud. Its formation is familiar to all of us, as it piles up in very dense, close masses, moving at times against the prevailing wind. As it develops, its silvery or coppery edges become more and more sharply outlined against the background of the sky.

It is interesting to watch this building-up process from the earliest stages. Its first appearance is in the form of a small, rather harmless-looking, cumulus cloud, rising up on the horizon of a blue sky. This steadily increases in size and density, and then begins to develop separate, Alpine-like peaks. These in turn will take on a rapidly darkening tint, sil-houetted against a sky that is now turning a dull yellow.

The thunder-heads will continue to increase at a fairly rapid rate of expansion, and will probably throw out other masses, spreading both vertically and horizontally. By now you can see a very dense black base of cloud stretching in one vast sheet at a low altitude across the sky, out of which the thunder-heads tower upwards, often to a consider-able height. Aircraft pilots who have attempted to fly above a thunder-storm have on occasions found that the central thunder-head had risen to an altitude of some 20,000 feet.

At this stage the storm is close upon us and vivid lightning flashes will begin to dart out from behind the banks of the cumulus clouds. These lightning flashes are charged, sparking across to one another from cloud to cloud, and from cloud to earth, and it is their inter-action with each other that produces the sound waves in the atmosphere that we know as thunder. The curious fact is that the upper part of a thunder-cloud is charged with positive electricity and the lower part with negative electricity, and the causes for this are explained later in this chapter. Lightning travels to the earth at the tremendous speed of 186,000 miles per second, but thunder merely travels leisurely along at only 12 miles a minute. It is therefore possible to work out how far away a storm may be.

There are two types of thunder-storm, the summer one and the winter one. The first is the more common, occurring usually within a warm air mass and when the earth's surface in that particular locality has become unduly hot. The winter type, which can take place any time of the year, forms along the edge of a strong cold front. The worst kind of thunder-storm is when the two types occur together, and this usually brings with it a trail of destruction, especially in the less temperate climes.

The severest storms of this nature are to be found in the tropics, but even in such temperate climes as the British Isles violent thunder-storms are experienced on occasions. An exceptional one was the storm that struck London less than a fortnight before the outbreak of the Second World War on 21st August, 1939. Both its intensity and duration were notable and a number of people were killed by lightning.

One of the most remarkable thunder-storms in the British Isles this century occurred in late autumn, and this was undoubtedly a combination of the two types. In November 1930, Shoeburyness, on the Essex coast, was almost without warning plunged into practically complete darkness at midday, the wind rose to near hurricane force, there was torrential rain with vivid thunder and continual lighting, and a strange roaring sound was heard rushing through the village. Within two minutes extensive damage was done.

In proportion to the number of thunder-storms throughout the world, lightning fatalities are comparatively low, and are the exception rather than the rule. The most outstanding case of this century was a thunder-storm in South Africa, when a flash of lightning struck a hut in which sixty-four natives were holding a party, and sixty-one were killed outright.

As air travel continues to expand, so does the record of aeroplanes being struck by lightning increase. It has been noticeable that such cases have been mainly when the plane has been flying through a hurricane-type cloud with a temperature either just above or just below freezing. Most lightning strikes on aircraft are preceded by an electrical discharge, visible at night, and known as St. Elmo's Fire.

Lightning, of course, does more damage to nature than to buildings, and certain trees are more susceptible than others, the oak being particularly so. Other trees which are struck fairly frequently are the elm, poplar and ash.

When a tree is struck the electric current runs up through the roots and trunk, and out through the branches and leaves. If this is a very high current the leaves will be scorched, but if the tree itself is struck the trunk will be damaged. It is not generally realised that a tree that is struck will sometimes affect the roots of other surrounding trees, with the result that they die also. Sometimes the tree-trunks are completely blown out by the lightning.

The tremendous force of the electric current in

lightning may be realised when we learn that it is of the order of 100 million volts.

A lightning flash is actually a spark that bridges the gap between two clouds, or between a cloud and the earth. In order for this spark to be made, there must be a *negative* charge of electricity in one place, and a *positive* charge in another. When these two charges meet each other, the lightning flash is produced.

The question now naturally arises: Why are some charges negative and some positive? This can best be answered by describing an experiment made by the famous meteorologist, Dr. G. C. Simpson. He took some drops of water and let them fall on to a metal plate, when it was found that they became charged with positive electricity, but the plate and atmosphere around were charged with negative electricity.

The same process happens in a thunder-storm. The raindrops—as described in a preceding chapter—are sometimes carried to very high levels, and increase in size all the time. When the large raindrops break up into smaller ones, the ascending air will carry to the top of the cloud a negative charge of electricity. The raindrops themselves, however, develop a positive charge, so that there is a process set up inside the cloud that goes on piling up negative electrical charges in one part, and positive charges in another.

The meeting of these charges in a violent storm gives us the type of discharge known as *Fork Lightning*. Its forked effect is due to the fact that it is discharged along a zigzag track through the atmosphere, which is the path of least resistance.

When you see that zigzag fork strike through the night sky, three things are happening. Firstly, a downward discharge develops about one million volts in barely one-millionth of a second! Secondly, a surge of high-volt electricity flashes back up the original path from the contact point on the earth's surface, in another minute fraction of a second. That is when people or objects on the ground are struck. Finally, a sustained charge between the cloud and the earth, lasting perhaps up to about one-tenth of a second, burns or melts the object struck.

It is very rare for lightning to strike vertically from cloud to earth, instead of zigzag; the atmospheric balance is maintained as a rule by the strokes which shoot horizontally from cloud to cloud. When a lightning flash is near the horizon, but is not actually visible except to light up the cloud or horizon, this is known as *Sheet Lightning*, and means that the flash was below the horizon many miles away.

The frequency of thunder-storms varies greatly in different parts of the world, and even in different parts of the British Isles. In our eastern counties, it averages about 20 days a year, but in northern Ireland and the Shetland Isles it is less than 5 days a year. Generally speaking, such storms are more frequent in hilly districts than in flat country, and very often a place which lies in the lee of a hilly area will escape the storm, which is broken up by the range of hills.

There is an idea that we often hear expressed that a thunder-storm will sometimes "return." This never really happens; when it seems as though the same storm stops in its tracks and comes back again, it is actually a new storm piling up in its immediate neighbourhood.

Some of the heaviest storms approach on a southerly wind, and you may have noticed that such a storm rarely comes up from any of the diagonal points of the compass; it will approach either from due west or due east.

How can you forecast a thunder-storm? If you find that the atmosphere has a high percentage of humidity (explained in the following chapter) at eight o'clock on a fine summer morning, this—if combined with a hot sun and a falling barometer—is likely to result in local thunder-storms by late afternoon or early evening.

As to predicting the direction a storm may take, a useful guide is to watch the course of the upper wind, about 2 or 3 miles high, as thunder-storms will normally move with that main current of air. The speed of these upper clouds will also give you some idea of the likely speed of the approaching storm; if they are moving fast, the storm will soon be upon you, but if they are slow moving, you will have a longer warning before it breaks.

It is sometimes believed that thunder-storms break up the weather, but this is another of those common fallacies. In fact, they do rather the reverse, because they help to restore the equilibrium of the atmosphere; after a storm of this nature the air becomes more stable (unless other storms are on the way), and replaces the previously unstable air that was heavily moisture-laden.

In the British Isles we are fortunate to experience no weather phenomena more violent than thunder-storms, as a general rule, although there are records from time to time of occasional tornadoes of the tropical variety.

A tornado must not be confused with a cyclone, as it so often is. The former has quite a small diameter, not more than 25 to 50 yards, whereas a cyclone may extend to a diameter of nearly 300 miles at times. The centre of a cyclone has a small area in which there is a cloudless sky and a dead calm. Round this calm centre the hurricane swirls, often accompanied by thunder and lightning. A cyclone

51

can cause damage over a much wider area than a tornado, but as a rule it is less severe.

A tornado has a central core of violently ascending currents of air, travelling mostly in a fairly straight path, and it is along this narrow path that terrific devastation is caused. An example of the power of Nature in such a storm is one that struck the town of Annapolis, Missouri, on 18th March, 1925. On a calm sunny afternoon there was suddenly seen a funnel-shaped intensely black cloud, like an inverted cone, appearing out of the clear sky on the horizon. At incredible speed it raced down on the town, bringing with it a wind that rose to the amazing speed of 150 miles an hour. With a roar like thunder it tore through the streets, levelling everything in its path. Solid stone buildings were split apart, oak trees 2 feet thick were uprooted like saplings, passenger trains were overturned and smashed, and fifty motor-cars were swept up into the air out of the street and carried over the roof-tops to be piled up in a heap of tangled wreckage in the fields beyond. The path of the storm was less than 300 yards wide, yet in its tracks it left what looked like a battlefield, with 823 people killed outright, and 2,990 injured!

Miniature tornadoes, arising from the same combination of weather conditions, have been reported from this country now and then—one of the worst of the century being the tornado that struck the north-east of Scotland in 1952.

Tornadoes are most frequent in the central areas of America, where the average is about fifty a year, and the other parts of the world where they are found (in their order of frequency) are the China Seas, Bay of Bengal, South Indian Ocean, West Indies, South Pacific, Arabian Sea and Australia. Tornadoes are caused by a cold wind overlapping a warm current.

The hurricane that swirls round a tropical cyclone derives its name from a Carib Indian word that means "big storm." In the north-western Pacific the tropical hurricane is called a Typhoon, and usually originates about 10 degrees north or south of the equator. It then sweeps northwards up the coast of North America and southward again towards Australia.

A storm that has many of the characteristics of the land tornado, but forms over the sea, is the waterspout. You will usually first see this appear as though hanging from the base of a very dark, dense nimbus cloud, in the shape of an inverted cone. This cone connects the cloud with the surface of the water.

A water-spout travels along as a column of whirling air, carrying with it a great quantity of water-drops, and having a core of torrential rain. You can sometimes see this in miniature form on a gusty day in a city street, in a whirling eddy of dust and leaves.

In the seas around the British Isles, water-spouts are generally of a comparatively mild nature, but like tornadoes they can be very violent in some of the tropical seas, and any shipping caught in their path is either sunk or severely damaged.

We are apt to believe that today we experience more violent upheavals of Nature than in past generations, but this is not so. Heavy storms and exceptional weather phenomena occurred much the same in past years as now. Today, however, with the advance of science and weather research, we have better and more accurate records of all that occurs, and with the Press of the world and the wireless, everyone reads and hears of any exceptional weather incidents in different parts of the globe.

CHAPTER VII

DEW, FROST AND FOG

AFTER a warm day in autumn, both the ground and the air immediately above it radiate their heat rapidly on a still, calm night, until the air cools to a temperature below what is known as "dewpoint."

It is necessary to understand this term clearly, because it is an important factor in certain weather observations. We know the dew is the aqueous vapour of the air deposited on surfaces that are cooled by radiation.

The amount of dew is dependent on the radiating and conducting powers of the particular surface, and on the degree of cold. Dew will fall heavily on grass and leaves, but only very lightly on earth, sand and gravel.

We have learned that a certain amount of water vapour is to be found in all the lower atmosphere. The higher the air temperature is, the greater in proportion is this amount of water vapour. When warm air is cooled there comes a point when condensation must take place (as explained in an earlier chapter), and this is termed "dewpoint."

The question then arises as to what controls that degree to which the temperature must fall to reach dewpoint. The answer is that it is according to the amount of humidity. If the air is dry it needs a greater fall of temperature to reach condensation level than if the air is very moisture-laden.

At all weather stations there are two thermometers, one of which is termed "wet bulb" and the other "dry bulb." The former is one in which the bulb containing the mercury is covered with a thin piece of wet muslin, evaporation from which lowers the reading. The latter is the ordinary thermometer with which we are all familiar, and has its bulb exposed in the usual way. The difference between the reading of the wet- and dry-bulb thermometers gives the amount of humidity, according to a standard scale. At normal temperatures a difference of 10 degrees indicates a relative humidity of approximately 50 per cent.

The difference between the "wet" and "dry" readings is sometimes very marked; e.g. on a typical July day the 6 p.m. "dry-bulb" reading may be 77°F., whereas the "wet-bulb" reading at the same hour may be only 60°F.

Evaporation takes place more rapidly when the air is drier, and thus the variation between the wet- and dry-bulb thermometers affords a good idea of the rate of evaporation. If your body is damp—such as during perspiration, or after bathing—the temperature which you feel is the wet-bulb one.

There is never any dew in cloudy weather, as the clouds prevent the escape of heat by radiation. Neither does dew occur in windy weather, because the wind prevents the temperature falling sufficiently low close to the ground. Heavy dews on summer nights usually indicate settled weather.

The heaviest dews are generally experienced during autumn nights when the air is still and the skies cloudless, and may sometimes be heavy enough to register an amount of water vapour equivalent to a light rainfall.

When the air cools to a temperature below "dew-point" we usually get a fog. This, however, is not the yellow pall-like fog of London and the industrial towns, but the white type of fog familiar to those living in the country. It is produced by a layer of warm air resting on a layer of cold air, which forms a kind of ceiling. This kind of fog is generally fairly persistent until stirred by the approach of wind.

Summer fogs, which form over valleys and fields adjoining rivers and streams—unlike winter fogs—do not extend upwards to any height, and although most ground objects may be obliterated from the aviator observer's view, the tops of the higher trees may be visible.

Another type is a coast fog. In certain kinds of weather the wind crosses an area of cold water where it is chilled to dewpoint and produces fog for a short way over the coast, but it does not extend far inland; it evaporates as it becomes warmed over the land. Coast fogs may occur at any time of the year—summer or winter. They are really clouds formed on the earth's surface, and are not often more than about 200 feet in thickness.

Usually a fog occurs only during an absence of wind, when the air is stagnant, but occasionally a damp fog or mist will be experienced when a strong breeze is blowing. If this happens, you may expect a period of rain to set in shortly.

The meteorological code that is used to denote the amount of visibility at any particular weather station is as follows:

0 Dense fog (objects not visible at 55 yards).
1 Thick fog (objects not visible at 220 yards).
2 Fog (objects not visible at 550 yards).
3 Moderate fog (objects not visible at 1,100 yards).
4 Mist or haze (objects not visible at 1¼ miles).
5 Poor visibility (objects not visible at 2½ miles).
6 Moderate visibility (objects not visible at 6¼ miles).
7 Good visibility (objects not visible at 12½ miles).

Plate 17. *A sky greying over in afternoon is seen in top picture, portending rain on the way. Lower picture shows a sky clearing after showers.*

Plate 18.   *Altostratus is the highest cloud of the stratus family.*

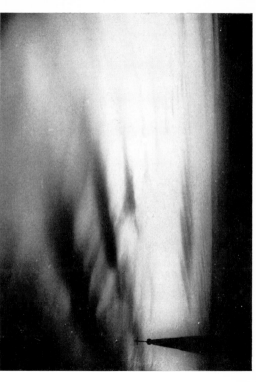

Plate 19. *The stratus cloud in very thin layers at a high altitude.*

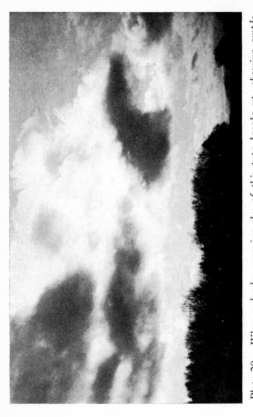

Plate 20. *When a leaden morning sky of this type breaks up, showing ample patches of blue, a bright, breezy day may be expected.*

Plate 21. *The nimbostratus rain cloud clearing after a heavy downpour.*

Plate 22.   *A storm sky clearing over Ben Alder.*

Plate 23. *A rain area spreading over from the west.*

Plate 24. Top: *A mixed sky of altocumulus and strato-cumulus.* Lower: *Pink-tinted clouds in the eastern sky at sunset are a stormy sign.*

Plate 25. A yellow sky at sunset, between clouds of greyish-purple, denotes rain and gales on the way.

Plate 26. *An example of fork lightning. The forked effect is due to a discharge along a zig-zag track through the atmosphere.*

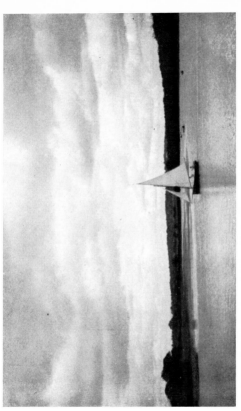

Plate. 27.　*A "rain sky" forming after a fine morning; a wet afternoon is imminent.*

Plate 28.   *Calm, fine weather returns as the rain area passes away.*

Plate 29. *Colours visible in a brilliant rainbow range from violet-blue, through green to yellow, orange and red.*

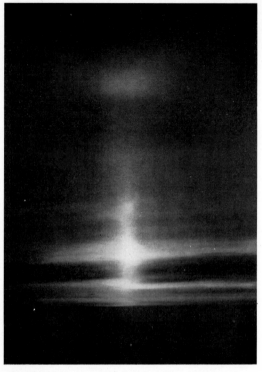

Plate 30. *An interesting example of a layer of cirro-*
stratus over the sun which has the effect of
producing a sun pillar.

Plate 31.　*Sunset over Southend pier.*

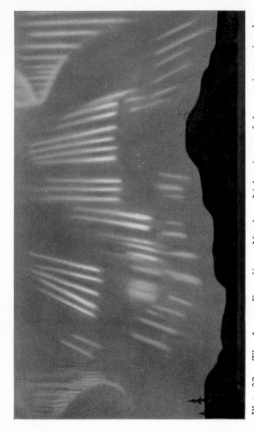

Plate 32. *The Aurora Borealis, or Northern Lights, is one of the most impressive sky spectacles.*

8 Very good visibility (objects not visible at 31
   miles).
9 Excellent visibility (objects visible beyond 31
   miles).

Various methods have been tried out to disperse
fog. These have included the letting-off of electrical
discharges into fog banks, and the spraying of
calcium chloride into a drifting fog. The last one is
the only method that has met with any considerable
success, and has been adopted in parts of America.
It is claimed to increase visibility from 500 to over
2,000 feet in three minutes.

"Fido"—as it was generally known—is no longer
used at our airports. It was in many respects a costly
and unsatisfactory procedure, as fog would quickly
form again over the surface of the runways as soon
as the air cooled after the igniting of hundreds of
gallons of petrol to heat the surrounding air. Radar
is, of course, the modern method for "blind" land-
ings, but when airports are fog-bound it is usual to
divert all aircraft to the nearest fog-free airport.

It will be a matter of surprise to most people to
learn that a dense sea fog will contain anything up
to 20,000 particles of water in every cubic inch.
Each particle is barely 1/25,000th part of an inch
in diameter. Even land fogs are saturated with water
vapour, and a typical London fog, that has now come
to be called "smog," may have more than 1 pint to
100 cubic yards, apart from the tons of soot and
dirt.

Mists are closely related to fogs. The most
familiar is the early morning mist—or haze—which
is the forerunner of a fine, warm day, and the late
evening mist, which rises as the air temperature
rapidly falls.

Spring and summer mists usually precede fine

weather, but certain types of autumn mists are often followed by rainy weather. Mists tend to hang about for longer periods over closely wooded country than over open slopes, as the temperature within the wooded area is lower.

Sometimes a mist will be confined to the upper air while it is quite clear below, and there is a kind of haze pall over the whole sky. This nearly always means a change in the weather, which may be from fair to wet, or from wet to fair (whichever type is being experienced at the time).

Misty mornings in early spring and late autumn are often accompanied by hoar frost. This occurs when the temperature on the ground falls below freezing-point, and the dew becomes converted into myriads of beautiful particles of all sorts of amazing designs that we see in hoar frost. As a rule, however, it is usually a sign of changeable weather, especially if it disappears without waiting for the sun's warmth upon it.

Very often a hoar frost will appear when the temperature of the air is still several degrees above freezing-point. This means that the thermometer on your garden wall about 4 or 5 feet above the ground may read as high as 40° F.

The ground does not really begin to freeze until the temperature is a degree or two below freezing-point, and it takes a fairly long spell of frost in this country to freeze the ground many inches. The one part of the world where the ground is almost continuously frozen, to an unbelievable depth, is in Spitzbergen and the Arctic Circle. Here it has been found frozen to a depth of *one thousand feet*.

Although it is always difficult to forecast the approach or duration of frosty spells, local forecasting of a frosty morning is comparatively simple to the careful observer. For instance, a still, cloudless night in late autumn, winter or early spring, with a rising barometer, is pretty sure to fall below freezing-point before dawn. If, however, there is a fairly high humidity and a moderate evening breeze, frost is unlikely.

A more severe type of frost, and one that usually lasts for a longer time, comes in on an easterly wind with overcast skies, and is known as a "black frost."

A frost which causes the greatest amount of disorganisation and accidents to vehicles and pedestrians is glazed frost. This is caused by rain falling from warmer air above, when the ground surface, and the air immediately above it, is below freezing-point. The cold layer remains for a time just a little distance above the ground, while the layer of moist and warm air above this also retains its temperature. The raindrops freeze immediately they strike the ground, and convert it into a sheet of ice. Similarly, tree branches, telegraph and telephone wires become heavily coated with solid ice, the weight of which sometimes breaks them down.

Aviators refer to this as an "ice storm," and this can at times be sufficient to bring disaster to the aircraft when the ice forms in considerable thickness on the wings.

We very rarely experience a glazed frost in the British Isles, and there have not been more than about three or four in London over the past ten years.

In America, however, it is much more common. An example of this is a remarkable storm that was recorded in New England in November 1921. On the Saturday afternoon, snow set in, after several sunny, frosty days, but this quickly changed to rain. The temperature, however, remained well below freezing-point, and the rain turned to ice as it fell. On Sunday the temperature fell to 25 degrees, and it continued raining with 7 degrees of frost. All night it rained heavily, and froze harder than ever, so that by Monday morning it was a world of ice. There was a coating of ice an inch thick over trees, buildings and roads, while at the same time the north-east wind increased to gale force. Still it rained, trees and telegraph wires began to fall everywhere, and traffic was brought to a standstill by the skating-rink roads. On Monday night it grew even worse. All electric power was cut off; cities and towns were in complete blackness; telephone and telegraph communication was cut off; streets were impassable to both vehicles and pedestrians. The dawn brought a sight of amazing destruction with a coating of ice at least 2 inches thick over everything. This gives some idea of the damage that can be done merely by the weight of ice.

The most severe frosts in the British Isles are experienced when there is an intense area of high pressure over northern Europe, and the great Siberian anticyclone moves farther westwards than normally. This distribution of pressure causes the low-pressure areas to move to the southward, thus opening up a channel for a direct flow of icy Continental or Arctic air to sweep across the greater part of these isles.

Calm, clear winter nights are always much colder in valleys than on higher slopes, and this is known as "valley inversions of temperature." These cold "pockets," or "frost-hollows," in the valleys rapidly increase in intensity of cold throughout the night. In fact, the bottom of a deep valley can become colder at night than any point in the open atmosphere up to some 10,000 feet above it.

There is one very noted frost-hollow in Britain, that has become almost world-famous in view of the truly remarkable temperatures continually being recorded there. This is not, as one might expect, in the northern half of the isles, but is in a district very close to London, at Rickmansworth, Hertfordshire.

The weather station there occupies a deep, sheltered valley at the foot of the Chiltern Hills. The mean minimum temperature is at or below freezing-point here for over seven months of the year, and readings below the freezing level are registered even in July and August! The mean *ground* minimum temperature is at or below freezing-point continuously for about three-fifths of the year, from 5th October to 12th May in an average year. Approximately 20 per cent of June nights record frost, 11 per cent of July nights, and 13 per cent of August nights.

Another interesting fact about this valley is that the range of temperature is very extreme. July days have been known to heat up in the afternoon to 91° F. after a morning temperature of 42°—a range of nearly 50 degrees in less than 12 hours! Meteorologists are fond of quoting this Hertfordshire valley as an example of climatic phenomena, as it is undoubtedly strange that within a dozen miles of London's outer suburbs there exists a place whose night climate is almost exactly "similar to that of the Aberdeenshire plateau, which is about the coldest inhabited region of the British Isles."

The most remarkable frost-hollow in the world is a small deep valley in the Austrian Alps, about 65 miles from Vienna. The valley is some 500 feet deep in a plateau, and the extreme winter temperatures for three successive winters were respectively 54, 60 and 60 degrees *below* zero F.! That means 92 degrees of frost! Yet the lowest temperature recorded on the summit of the mountain, 10,200 feet up, was 58 degrees warmer!

Frosts are one of the main worries of the fruit grower, for whom the Meteorological Office issues special frost warnings for given districts. There has been a tendency of late years for frosts in Britain to continue later into the spring than formerly, many places reporting ground frosts up till the end of May or even early June. If the temperature falls below freezing-point during these spring nights, and remains at that level for several hours, the blossom and fruitlets can be ruined.

The observer, however, should note how the degree of damage to fruit trees depends on the type of weather that accompanies these low temperatures. If the frost follows close after rain, when the leaves are covered with films of water, the damage is more severe than if the night is dry. Also, if the temperature falls very suddenly after sunset, and the morning thaw is equally sudden, the damage again is greater than if the temperature change were more gradual.

Some British woodland trees are also susceptible to frosts, and these include beech, spruce and Douglas fir. That is why you will find that these trees are usually planted in the most sheltered positions. Horse-chestnut, sycamore and hawthorn are among our more hardy trees, but the hardiest of all are elm, lime, birch, alder, hazel, hornbeam and Scots pine. None of these are affected at all by the degree of frost experienced in Britain, even in our most severe winters.

CHAPTER VIII

OTHER WEATHER PHENOMENA

CLOUDS and sunset colours undoubtedly provide some of the most wonderful spectacles of Nature, but there are also other weather phenomena that far surpass anything that man can devise on the earth below.

Who can fail to be thrilled by the beauty of the rainbow? That mysterious arc of many colours calls forth exclamations of wonder and admiration from the most materially minded people.

As we all know, the rainbow is associated with showery weather, and always appears in the opposite point of the compass to the sun. It is caused by the sun's reflection on a cloud of raindrops. What happens is that the sunlight passes through these raindrops, and as it does so it is broken up into a number of components, each of which corresponds to one of the many colours.

We are usually able to see two bows; the larger one is called the "secondary" and the smaller one the "primary" bow. In each bow the colours occur is reverse order. Those usually visible are:

Primary (reading from outer band): Red, violet or blue.
Secondary: Violet or blue, red.

Sometimes we are lucky enough to see a particularly brilliant rainbow, and then there are visible seven colours that vary between violet-blue, green-yellow or orange, and red. On the ground we are only able to observe the half-circle, but if we were in an aeroplane at a sufficiently high altitude at such a time, we would be able to see the wonderful spectacle of a complete rainbow circle.

When a rainbow appears after the first shower during a spell of fine weather, it is usually a sign of a coming change to a more unsettled type. During an unsettled spell, a rainbow appearing in the evening, reflected on clouds passing away from the west to the east, usually denotes an improvement on the morrow.

Some of the most beautiful sky spectacles are caused by dust particles in the atmosphere and molecules of the air on which the sun's rays fall. Very occasionally you may see a phenomenon known as a "sun pillar." This appears as a column of either red or white light extending vertically above and below the sun, and this is sometimes crossed by a similar horizontal bar. When it forms a complete cross in this manner, it is called the "heavenly cross," but it is not seen very often in the British Isles. A sun pillar is caused by the reflection of the sun's rays on the vertical sides of columnar crystals in the atmosphere. Under similar conditions, a "moon pillar" is occasionally seen.

During a showery spell you may sometimes observe lines of watery-looking light radiating from the sun. We speak of this as "the sun drawing water," and the meteorological term for this is "crepuscular rays."

A fairly common spectacle is that of a sun or moon halo or corona.

Very often a halo is confused with a corona, but the two are really quite distinct. A halo is seen when the sun or moon shines through a thin whitish veil of cirrostratus and is produced by the refraction of the light of the sun or moon through ice crystals in the atmosphere.

It appears as a faint ring around the sun or moon

and varies in size and colour. The space within the ring appears less bright than that just outside. When the halo is very faint the ring appears white, but if it is more strongly defined you are able to see a red tint on the inner edge and yellow on the outer.

A corona is associated with altocumulus cloud. It is smaller in diameter than a halo, and is produced by the diffraction of the light rays by small water particles in the cloud. The colours of the corona fall in the reverse order from those of the halo, the red being on the outside of the ring.

A corona may consist of a single ring or two or three consecutive ones. These rings are quite geometrically exact; the diameter of the second ring is double that of the inner one, and if there is a third ring this is three times the diameter of the inner one.

Whereas a halo is nearly always followed by rain, it is not always so with the corona. If this is observed to be growing smaller, it is a sign that the vapour globules are becoming larger and will presently fall to the earth in the form of rain.

If, however, the diameter of the corona begins to grow larger, the weather will become fine, because the vapour globules are evidently getting smaller and the moisture in the atmosphere is decreasing.

Many people have the idea that a corona is only to be seen around the moon, but this is not so. A sun corona, however, can only be seen through tinted glasses, because the sunlight itself is too dazzling for the naked eye.

Although most haloes and coronae are circular about the sun or moon, this is not always the case, as some pass through the sun and others are circular about the zenith. Occasionally in very cold weather, where ice crystals are to be found in the lower part of the atmosphere, the refraction produces phenomena known as "mock" suns and moons. These are not often seen in the British Isles, although I have on two occasions witnessed very good spectacles of a "mock" sun. They are more frequent, however, in the Arctic regions.

Another sky phenomenon is known as the Green Ray, which is sometimes to be seen. It appears as a very brilliant emerald coloration on the very last edge of the setting sun, or the very first edge of the rising sun.

There is also a glow sometimes seen in the sky opposite the sun, only slightly lighter than the general sky illumination, and roughly circular or elliptical, which goes by the strange name of the Gegenschein.

The most magnificent sky spectacle of all is the Aurora Borealis, sometimes called the Northern Lights. It is very rarely seen in southern Europe, but is a phenomenon more common to the northern climes, and the farther north one goes the more brilliant it becomes. It is seen not infrequently in Scotland, and every one of the present generation will remember the outstanding display, such as has probably never before been seen in Britain, that occurred during the night of January 25th–26th, 1938. This was the greatest auroral display within living memory, and was seen over nearly the whole of Europe, and even as far south as Madeira and Bermuda, which was unprecedented. The aurora in this instance was accompanied by a magnetic storm of unusual intensity, and was first seen in south-east England about 6.15 in the evening, and continued until 1 a.m. Meteorologists noted that the chief features of this display were the continual and rapid changes, the variety of auroral types, and the splendour of the colour effects.

Just before 7 p.m. there was a development of brilliant red rays, which people all over Britain at first mistook for some great fire. Later, these red rays reached a great altitude above the horizon, radiating from all parts of the auroral arc. At another period of the evening—which was starlit nearly all the time—the red colour gave place to a greenish-white and greenish-yellow, which brightened the heavens almost like dawn.

The rays showed a remarkable variety of length, shape and width, and changed in form from defined isolated rays to great bundles of different colours. Shortly after 7 p.m. an even more spectacular phenomenon occurred. From the upper edge of the lower arc there suddenly flashed out in quick succession from east to west electrical discharges similar to brush discharges, which continued for a quarter of an hour, culminating in a sort of mighty flame-lit canopy that hung nearly vertically from the heavens like a huge curtain.

Auroral displays are attributed to the entry of particles from outer space into the earth's atmosphere, but this is merely an assumption, and scientists have not yet solved the real mystery of this phenomenon. It is believed that such particles probably originate from the sun, are electrically charged, and travel downwards in streams which carry almost equal numbers of positive and negative charges.

The height to which the aurora extends has never been established, although it is known that it is rarely less than 50 miles, and at times several hundred miles upwards. There is no way of predicting the occurrence of such displays, which will appear suddenly for no particular reason, but it has been noticed that on the whole they tend to be more frequent in years of high sun-spot activity.

An interesting sky spectacle seen occasionally is known as the Zodiacal Light. This is a glow that appears in the western sky just after twilight, and is much more striking and strange than the normal sunset glow. It is also seen sometimes in the eastern sky just before dawn. This glow illuminates the sky in that quarter of the horizon in the shape of an ellipse, with its axis inclined to the horizon. The cause of this phenomenon has been considered as due to the reflection of sunlight from small meteoric particles, but some scientists have lately thrown doubt on that theory, and are inclined to believe it is more likely an ionisation effect.

Considerable quantities of dust in the air, such as may occur after some volcanic or similar eruption of sufficient magnitude, will often cause strange sky spectacles. A blue sun was reported from many parts of the world after the great Krakatoa eruption. The sun appeared during the midday hours, shining a deep azure blue; at sunrise it was a bright light blue, and at sunset a dark blue. Indeed, it produced a most remarkable effect. This was caused by the sun shining through the dense collection of dust particles in the upper atmosphere, which had been carried to a great height as a result of the eruption.

A blue sun has also been reported shining through the haze for two or three days at a time after some of the great dust-storms over the Sahara and other wide desert areas. Sometimes the colour is yellow, however, and following on a great dust-storm over Cairo, the sun shone through a pale yellow colour, while the tints in the area immediately around it were pale blue. At night, the moon was also pale yellow, but with a similar blue circle round it.

Among other types of unusual weather phenomena must be mentioned coloured rain and snow. Rain has been known to fall as red or blue. It is unusual is this country, but rather less so abroad.

In March 1935, blue rain was reported from the Shetland Isles, after a heavy thunder-storm, and was described as looking very much like blue-black ink diluted with water. The explanation of this was given as being due to the particular atmospheric conditions in that locality, which at the time were highly polluted. These conditions were extremely unusual, as there was unstable air above a stable layer, combined with a mass of cold air previously moving in the opposite direction. Even in the early stages of the storm the warm air was three-quarters surrounded by cold air, the latter having arrived on a south-easterly wind.

There have been numerous reports of coloured rain from Italy, and on one occasion a shower of red rain fell at Bordighera. At the time there was a current of hot, moist air blowing from the east, and the preceding hours had been rainy and overcast.

Red rain has also been reported from New Zealand. One such occasion was 26th October, 1929. For two days preceding this phenomenon the whole of the South Island was enveloped in a curious tinted, smoky haze, and this disappeared after the storm of red rain. It was considered to have originated in Australia, and was repeated a month later.

The only time that red rain has fallen over England was on 21st and 23rd February, 1903. It was believed due to the raindrops being coloured by dust blown across the Sahara in a great storm, and carried northwards to Europe.

Coloured snow has also been similarly reported from various parts of the world, usually red or green, but occasionally yellow or brown. These colours are caused by minute vegetable organisms known as Protococcus Nivalis.

CHAPTER IX

INSTRUMENTS FOR THE WEATHER OBSERVER

ONE of the most familiar weather instruments, to be found in many households, is the ordinary aneroid barometer that hangs on the wall. It consists of a flat, round metal box that has been emptied of air. The atmosphere presses the top and bottom of the box towards one another, according to whether the pressure is high or low.

This is shown on the "clock" face of the barometer, that has a scale of readings in inches of mercury, ranging on most instruments from 28 inches to 31 inches. On the outer rim is a guide as to the weather to be expected at the different readings: "Stormy"—"Rain"—"Change"—"Fair"—"Very Dry."

Although the meteorologist requires instruments of greater precision, the aneroid barometer is sufficiently accurate for the average householder. Yet it is often subject to a good deal of scathing criticism and slander when, although the indicator points to "Very Dry" it may be raining outside, or when it points to "Rain," the sun is shining from a clear blue sky.

Many people become quite infuriated on such occasions; however, it is not the barometer that is at fault, but the householder, who has not taken the trouble to study the reasons for the behaviour of the barometer under certain conditions.

You must not assume that because the barometer is high it will be a fine day, or because it is low it will be rainy. The important thing to observe is whether it is rising or falling.

Let us take an actual example. One morning, when you get up, say, about 7 o'clock, you notice the barometer reading is at 30·1 inches, i.e. "Fair," but before you have finished your breakfast it has started to rain, and it keeps on steadily all morning. When you tap the barometer, however, you notice it is falling very decidedly, and another glance at about 10 o'clock shows it is now down to 30 inches, but still in the "Fair" section, and continuing to fall. This means that a depression has reached your area round about 8 to 9 a.m. and will probably not clear until late afternoon at the earliest.

On the other hand, you may notice on another morning that the barometer is down to 29·4 inches, in the "Rain" section, but it is quite dry and fine, although probably dull and cloudy. A tap, however, shows that the glass is rising. By 10 o'clock it has jumped up to 29·5 inches and is still rising steadily. This shows that the main centre of the depression, which caused a rainy night, has passed, and by the middle of the morning you may expect the sun to break through, and be followed by a bright afternoon.

You will see, then, that one morning you had it rainy when the barometer was actually six-tenths of an inch higher than the fine morning (and that is a considerable range on the barometer). So you can have a fine day on a low barometer that is rising, if the wind has veered from south-west to north-west, and a wet day on a high barometer that is falling, if the wind has backed from north-west to south-west or south-east. For this reason, you can be entirely misled if you rely only on the readings without taking into account all the other signs.

A type of barometer commonly seen in Victorian households was the simple glass tube, sealed at one end, and fixed perpendicularly with the open end

71

immersed in a small bulb filled with mercury. As the atmospheric pressure changed, so the column of mercury rose or fell, and the readings showed at the side of the column were also in inches of mercury. The top of the column read 31 inches, and the bottom 28 inches, thus giving the same range as the aneroid barometer.

A more sensitive instrument than the ordinary barometer is the barograph. I have used one for the past 30 years, and I have found that it indicates a coming change somewhat earlier than my barometer that hangs in the same room.

The aneroid barograph works on the same principle as the barometer. It consists of a battery of vacuum boxes fixed to the base, and connected with a movable lever at the top. The springs in the boxes expand when the pressure on them is reduced, that is to say, when the pressure falls. There is a revolving clock cylinder (it works like a clock), round which is fixed a weekly graph, and on which a long pen arm records the movement. This graph is renewed every seven days, and shows at a glance what the weather has been doing during the past week; what day and at what hour, for instance, an unsettled spell sent the arm on the graph down with a decided dip, or if there was a dry spell when it jumped high up the graph. You can see just how long each rise or fall lasted, and whether these were sudden or gradual; or it may have been a week of very uniform weather, in which case the line on the graph will be pretty steady.

The barometer or barograph should be used in conjunction with other weather observations, particularly the wind. It is noticeable that when the wind is blowing from a westerly direction, the barometer will frequently not begin to fall until the rain has actually started; in other words, the barometric change *accompanies* the change of weather. But if the wind is in an easterly direction, the barometric change definitely *precedes* the weather change.

When the barometer is high and steady with a north-west wind, this usually means several days of fine weather. But a north-west wind, backing west, with the barometer rising too rapidly, means a day—or perhaps two—of fair, warm weather, followed by rain. This is owing to the fact that the rise is caused by a ridge of high pressure passing across the country, with a depression in its wake, as explained in Chapter II.

Sometimes the barometer will fall without being followed immediately by rain. In that case the fall denotes a high wind, and a severe gale may be expected if this fall is rapid. After the wind abates rain will probably fall, but this is sometimes as long as 48 hours after the first fall of the barometer begins.

It is always a bad sign if a falling barometer is accompanied by a rising temperature, as it denotes that the atmosphere is becoming more charged with moisture, and unsettled weather is on the way.

Conversely, if the barometer rises steadily, and the temperature falls, fairer weather is indicated, with the wind veering to a more northerly quarter.

You should beware of too rapid a rise of the barometer, because this means that the improvement in the weather will only be temporary. A gradual rise, accompanied by a dry atmosphere, denotes more prolonged settled weather. In the same way, a gradual fall (especially if the weather still continues fair for some days) foretells a long unsettled spell.

There are certain conditions when the barometer does not fall—for snow, which is sometimes driven over the British Isles on an easterly wind from an anticyclone on the Continent.

It is very rare for the barometer to reach the top

reading in this country and I have only twice recorded it on my barograph in the last 40 years. The highest reading ever recorded in England was on 9th January, 1896, of 31·013, near Chester, and in Scotland on the same day, of 31·106 at Fort William.

The barometer was invented by Torricelli, the famous Italian scientist. Through his experiments was discovered the existence of atmospheric pressure. He thought it possible that other fluids might behave in the same way as water, which rises in a pump because of the pressure of the atmosphere. He took the heaviest of all fluids, which is mercury, and experimented to find out whether that would rise in the same way. Filling a fine glass tube with mercury, he turned it upside-down in a cup that already contained mercury. He then found that instead of the mercury running out of the tube there was some force that held it up. He realised that this was the atmospheric pressure pressing down on the surface of the mercury in the cup and forcing it up into the glass tube.

Another discovery in this direction was by Pascal, who found that atmospheric pressure varied at different heights. He ascended to a considerable height in a balloon, with one of Torricelli's tubes, and discovered that up there the level of the mercury was much lower. The level rose as he descended, thus proving the fall of pressure with height. This, of course, is what causes the difficulty of breathing at great heights, such as in the Mount Everest expeditions. With many people it also causes mountain sickness.

Another equally familiar instrument is the thermometer. This was invented more than 300 years ago by Galileo. The first thermometer was a simple glass tube ending in a bulb, the tube being heated and placed upside-down in a vessel of water. As the heated air inside the tube began to cool, the water ran up it, and the water-level therefore gave a very rough idea of the temperature of the air.

This was not a very satisfactory instrument, because of its lack of accuracy, and also owing to the fact that it was subject to any changes in atmospheric pressure. Some 50 years later it was found that much greater accuracy was obtained by closing the tube entirely after heating and alcohol was introduced in place of water. In the year 1670 mercury was used.

Most weather observers—professionals or amateurs—use a self-registering thermometer for outdoor readings. This instrument has a tube of double length bent half-way so that it forms a "U" shape with the two columns exactly parallel and with a bulb at each end, instead of the single vertical glass tube. One column gives the maximum day temperature reading, and the other the minimum night temperature, by means of steel indices which slide up and down each column and which are set daily with a magnet.

The usual and most suitable hours at which to take readings of the thermometer are 6 a.m., midday, 6 p.m., midnight, which provides as accurate a mean as possible for the 24 hours.

The amateur observer naturally does not find it easy to take readings at these somewhat awkward hours, as it is not very convenient to walk up your garden at midnight to make an observation. In this case, adjust the hours as near as possible to these official ones to arrive at as accurate a mean temperature as possible.

On a summer's day, the maximum temperature is normally between 4 and 5 p.m., and the minimum between 3 and 4 a.m. In winter-time the maximum temperature is between 1 and 2 p.m., and the minimum between 6 and 7 a.m.

The position of the thermometer is important. For instance, if it is fixed to a brick wall or on some object that attracts the heat of the sun and is sheltered from the breeze, it is impossible to obtain a true shade temperature. The best position is suspended from a tree branch in the garden in a spot which the sun does not reach, and where it can have a free circulation of air all round it.

All thermometer readings reported in the newspapers and over the radio are shade temperatures, and sun readings are only taken for particular purposes. It is, however, interesting to know how high the midsummer sun can raise the thermometer, and I have known it to register as high as 160° F. on the sandy heathland of the Bisley Rifle Ranges in Surrey. The ordinary outdoor thermometer cannot be used to register these high sun temperatures, but a special thermometer is necessary which has a black bulb mounted in a glass tube exhausted of air. This makes it possible for the intensity of the sun's radiant heat to be accurately measured.

Since 1st January 1961 the Meteorological Office has used only the Centigrade scale of temperature, in the interest of international co-operation. This scale, however, has proved less popular than Fahrenheit among many of the general public and the farming community, as a result of which both scales are at present shown in weather reports in the newspapers.

It is not too difficult for the amateur observer to make his own thermometer. In order to do this, take a fine glass tube with a bulb at one end, fill the bulb and part of the tube with mercury, and then immerse the bulb in boiling water. Vapour is thus formed which travels up the tube and pushes away the air in front of it. Now close the end of the tube and leave the mercury to cool. The latter can then expand or contract freely in either direction in the empty space above the level in the tube. The more the mercury swells with heat, the higher it rises in the tube, and the cooler it becomes, the more it falls. The temperature readings must then be marked by checking the levels with an accurate thermometer.

For recording temperatures over a period, there is an instrument known as the thermograph on the same lines as the barograph already described. This is self-registering, the pen on the chart around the drum giving a continuous reading of the temperature throughout the 24 hours of each day.

An extension of this idea is the baro-thermograph, which combines the readings of both barometer and thermometer in the one instrument and records on the same chart barometric pressure and temperature.

A further combination is the baro-thermo-hygrograph. This instrument records on the one chart the separate readings of barometric pressure, temperature and humidity.

The instrument that is used to measure humidity only is known as the hygroscope or hair hygrometer. It consists of a 4-inch diameter case beneath which is a slotted tube. In the tube are mounted oil-free human hairs or other organic tissue which changes its length when it absorbs moisture. As the moisture in the atmosphere increases, so do the hairs lengthen in proportion. An adjustment screw is provided at the lower end of the case to which the hairs are fixed, and at the top end a link piece is connected direct to a crank on the pointer spindle.

On the instrument are two scales: one that gives the relative percentage humidity readings and the other the dewpoint. All official observers check this instrument periodically by making the hairs wet, when a reading of approximately 95 per cent should be shown.

Another instrument of this nature has the some-what curious name of a whirling hygrometer. This consists of two thermometer tubes mounted side by side with a handle that enables the hygrometer to be whirled rapidly in the air. The instrument should be rotated at a rate of not less than 120 a minute, so that an air speed of not less than 15 feet a second past the wet bulb can be obtained. It should be whirled for about 30 seconds and then stopped, and the wet-bulb reading taken first. This should be repeated four times to obtain a mean reading.

There is a very handy type of this instrument in pocket size, which is particularly useful for taking humidity readings when travelling about. The tubes are only 6 inches long, with a scale 4 inches long, and mounted on an aluminium frame with folding handle. There is also a 4-inch dial pocket hair hygro-meter in a 4½-inch diameter metal case. The dial is enamelled white with black divisions and figures.

A specially designed hygrometer is used for measuring dewpoint. This has thermometers 15 inches long mounted in nickel-plated sheaths, one bulb being immersed in a polished solid silver thimble. The latter is connected to a filler containing ether, to which is attached a rubber pipe and bulb. As the air is drawn through the ether by means of this rubber bulb, the thimble is slowly cooled and dew eventually forms on it, at which stage the thermometer reading is taken.

The next important instrument to consider is the wind velocity recorder, known as an anemometer, which incorporates, in the direction-finding portion, the more familiar wind vane. It is necessary to take a good deal of care in selecting a suitable site for this instrument, as there should be no trees or buildings that shelter the anemometer, and the minimum height of the head of the instrument should be 20 feet above the roof. This compares with the minimum height required for an ordinary wind vane, which is 10 feet. In passing, it is worth noting that when setting up a wind vane on your roof, you must take extreme care to make quite sure that it is properly orientated to the true north and not the magnetic north.*

There are several types of anemometer, all of which are first tested in the wind channel of the National Physical Laboratory before being released for general use. One of the best known is the Dines' pressure tube anemometer. It was the outcome of a long series of experimental investigations into the relations between the velocity and pressure of the wind, carried out by Mr. W. H. Dines, B.A., F.R.S., past-president of the Royal Meteorological Society, and has since been confirmed by numerous wind-tunnel tests.

The construction of the instrument is extremely simple. It consists of two independent parts—the head, which is the part exposed to the wind, and the recording apparatus, which may be set up in any convenient place indoors, and, if necessary, at a considerable distance from the head; these two parts are connected with each other by two metal tubes, either flexible or rigid.

The head consists of a vane formed of a horizontal tube open at one end, and supported upon the top of a vertical tube into which it leads. Just below the vane this vertical tube is surrounded by another of much larger diameter, the exterior of which is perforated by four rings of holes placed close together around its circumference.

The recorder comprises a float, which is a specially

---

* True north is the direction of the North Pole from the observer. Magnetic north is the direction in which the compass needle points. The angle between true and magnetic north is known as Magnetic Variation.

shaped copper vessel closed at one end; it is placed with its open end downwards in a vessel partially filled with water and sealed from the air of the room in which it is situated.

The vane is kept with its open end facing the wind, and every increase in the wind pressure is transmitted through it down the vertical tube and through the connecting pipe to the inside of the float, which is caused to rise. The outer perforated tube below the vane is connected by means of the second pipe to the top of the closed vessel containing the float. As the wind blows across the perforations, the air in the tube is sucked out, with the result that a reduction of pressure takes place in the vessel above the float, simultaneously with the increase of pressure within it. The two forces thus act together, but in opposite ways, to produce the same effect, namely, to raise the float in the water. As the wind pressure decreases the float falls again by its own weight until an equilibrium is established between it and the diminished pressure.

Attached by a flange to the top of the float is a tubular rod which passes through what is practically an air-tight collar in the cover of the water vessel; this rod carries a pen, the point of which rests against a sheet of paper attached to a drum which is rotated by a clock mechanism. With every upward or downward movement of the float, corresponding to an increase or decrease of wind force, the pen leaves a trace upon the paper, and thus the amount of every variation in the strength of the wind is graphically registered, together with the time of its occurrence.

The curve of the centre portion of the float is calculated mathematically according to the law governing the relation of pressure to wind velocity, and is such that the velocity curve on the chart is a straight line. The float is accurately made and balanced, and is capable of recording the smallest variations of velocity at any part of the scale.

The record not only gives the average velocity of the wind over a given time, but also records each variation in the force of the wind, so that the strength of the gusts and the frequency of their occurrence can be read at once. In cases of damage done by wind these data are often of importance, whilst to the meteorologist the traces afford information concerning "the internal structure of the wind" which no other form of anemometer gives.

These anemometers were used on such famous explorations as the National Antarctic Expedition, Scott's Expedition, 1910, and Shackleton's Expedition, 1914.

A wind direction recorder is a valuable addition to a wind velocity recorder, and no such instrument can now be considered complete unless fitted with it.

The simplest of all comprises only a single pen, and gives a record on the same chart and to the same time-scale as the Dines' pressure tube anemometer. Other instruments of this type have twin pens and these are used at the Air Ministry Meteorological Office.

Among many other types of anemometers is a very convenient little instrument known as the hand-held cup anemometer. This is most convenient for general use as it is sufficiently portable to carry about. Three readily detachable arms with light alloy cups are mounted on a spindle running in ball-bearings. These bearings are sealed and hold sufficient oil to last over a long period of time.

Another instrument of this nature is known as the diaphragm indicating anemometer. These instruments give an immediate reading of wind speed on a dial. They can be placed any distance, not exceeding 100 feet, from the wind vane or head. The pressure and suction pipe connections are made with standard unions at each end. The pipes are of thick walled copper to allow bending so that they may conform to installation conditions. Owing to the small displacement of the diaphragm, the readings show an immediate response to the gusts and lulls in the wind.

An interesting invention is the electric wind indicator, which allows one to sit indoors and watch the wind changes on a wall recorder. It comprises a roof weather vane, with a cable leading down to an electrically illuminated indicator on the wall, via a transformer connected to the ordinary lighting system. The cable connects the vane contacts to the eight direction lamps in the indicator box which is of polished hardwood. For the purpose of measuring wind speed a ninth lamp and buzzer are fitted in the cabinet so that signals from any electric contact anemometer may be received and timed. Switches are provided to cut off the current except when indication of direction or velocity is required.

The weather vane, of stainless steel, is quite small, and rotates on ball-bearings. It is very sensitive to any wind change. A carbon contact bar is attached to the weather-vane shaft, passing over eight copper segments at eight different wind directions:

North—north-east—east—south-east—south—south-west—west—north-west.

The electric current consumption burning at only 4 volts is almost negligible. The wind-indicator clock has constantly changing light circles, which show exactly—and absolutely noiselessly—the correct direction of the prevailing wind at any particular moment.

In certain circumstances danger may arise to buildings if the wind exceeds a given velocity. For this purpose there is a wind alarm apparatus which consists of a Dines' rotating wind vane fixed to the structure in a suitably exposed position and connected by pipes to a weatherproof iron-cased anemometer. In this iron case is fitted a white bulb, which remains alight as long as the mains are connected, and a red bulb to give visible warning that the wind has exceeded the set speed.

Another very essential instrument is the rainfall gauge, of which there are several types. The principle is the measurement of the depth of water that would be collected upon a level area of any size, supposing the rain to fall uniformly over the area at the rate at which it falls into the gauge. The gauge must be placed in a suitable position, clear of any tree drippings, and not exposed to strong winds which might cause the water to ripple over the rim and give inaccurate readings.

The earliest instrument of this type was the Korean rain gauge invented in 1442 when the importance of rainfall on crops was first fully realised. This gauge is on exhibition at the Science Museum at South Kensington. The first European rain gauge was invented in 1639 by an Italian, Benedetto Castelli.

The simplest type of modern rain gauge consists of a copper funnel, about 5 inches in diameter, which is inserted into a glass or metal receiver that collects the rain. The funnel has to be carefully constructed so as to prevent any heavy rain splashing out.

One of the most satisfactory types of gauge is a brass tube just over 2 inches in diameter, which is fitted inside an 8-inch cylindrical can with a funnel cover to reduce any evaporation loss.

In countries where excessive rainfalls occur, such as Hawaii, the rainiest place in the world (where in one day will be experienced a rainfall greater than the highest mean rainfall recorded in England in a whole year), special rainfall gauges have to be constructed, and these are naturally the largest in the world.

In certain parts of America there are automatic radio rain gauges. These are most interesting instruments, as they collect rainfall in the ordinary way and at intervals automatically broadcast by a modified Morse code signal the amount of rainfall the gauge has collected.

A particular type of rainfall gauge used by water engineers is known as the hyetograph, which records the duration as well as the intensity of rainfall. A 6-inch diameter funnel leads the rain through a pipe to a float chamber. There is a pen arm similar to that which has been described with the barograph, and this arm is lifted by a rod attached to the float through a device constructed by means of a stud and palette. When the pen arm reaches the top of the chart, it disengages from the stud and the arm falls back to the bottom of the chart. The palette then engages with the next stud and continues to repeat the operation until the container is full. These gauges have a maximum capacity of 4 inches of rainfall, and the daily chart is fitted to an 8-day clock drum.

One problem that arises in regard to rain gauges is during periods of frost. To avoid the rain in the gauge freezing, a small nightlight is usually placed inside, which is sufficient to prevent this happening.

Snow can also be measured in the ordinary rainfall gauge on melting. This gives the water content of the snowfall, or, in other words, the amount of the fall in terms of rainfall. It is usual to take three distinct measurements of snow, and, in addition to that already mentioned, the total depth of the snow on the ground and the depth of each separate snow-fall is taken. These measurements are taken by simply inserting a special measure stick in several different places and then taking the mean reading.

Many people have the mistaken idea that a given depth of snow is equivalent to a given amount of rainfall. This, however, is not so. For instance, 1 inch rainfall equivalent may be produced by only 4 inches of tightly packed wet snow at the bottom of a drift. It may take as much as 1½ feet of dry powdery snow at the top of a drift to give the same amount of water content.

A very near neighbour of the rainfall gauge is the evaporation gauge, which is used to measure the degree of evaporation. Evaporation is the name we give to the physical process by which liquid water becomes water vapour. When water vapour in the air condenses, it falls in the form of rain, hail or snow.

The evaporation gauge consists of a glass tube about 9 inches long, with the measurements in centimetres. A disc of porous paper is held by a metal clip and from this disc the water in the tube evaporates, the degree of evaporation being shown by the alteration of level. This gauge is known as the evaporimeter.

Another kind is the index type, consisting of a copper float which rises and falls in a copper cylinder, the latter acting as a still-water chamber. A brass wheel is operated by a chain attached to the float, turning an index hand attached to the axis. The index hand moves over an arc of 9½ inches radius on which the scale registers up to 4 inches. This scale is clearly engraved on a brass strip attached to the iron frame.

Before we leave the rainfall gauge group, there is lastly an instrument known as the recording percolation gauge. This is used to record the percolation of rainfall through the earth. The gauge comprises a copper tank, 18 inches in diameter and 3 feet high, with a gauge glass for measuring accurately the volume of water in the tank. A copper float, 8 inches in diameter, moves in the tank and operates one or more pen arms by a cable and pulley device. The chart is on the same revolving cylinder principle as the previous instruments described, making one revolution every 24 hours. A suitable site is selected for the percolation gauge, and under the ground is installed a large trough. The gauge is placed in a tunnel and the trough collects the water and records the amount of rainfall percolation on the clock-driven chart.

The last instrument with which we are concerned is the sunshine recorder. There are two types, one of which simply measures the number of hours of bright sunshine per day, and the other which measures the intensity of the sun's rays.

There are three varieties of the former instrument. The first is an electrical recorder consisting of a large black bulb filled with air enclosed in a glass sheath from which all air has been removed so as to protect the bulb from atmospheric temperatures. As the sun's rays reach it the air in the bulb expands. When the rays are bright enough to be classified as "Bright Sunshine" a short column of mercury moves upward to reach and connect two wires set in the glass. An electrical current passes and moves a pen on the sunshine recording chart on the drum.

The second kind is operated by means of burning. This will no doubt be familiar to many of you who have experimented with a piece of paper and a magnifying glass in the summer sun. A glass bulb focuses the rays of the sun on a thick strip of cardboard marked off in hours and minutes. Bright sunshine burns a defined groove on this cardboard. If the sunshine is merely weak and pale, the chart is only slightly discoloured.

The third kind is the photographic type which traces arcs of circles as the earth turns, so long as the sky remains clear. The advantage of this type is that it can also be used to record the amount of night cloudiness.

The sunshine recorder used for measuring the intensity of the sun's rays is known as a pyrheliometer. This, however, is a very specialised instrument which is only used for particular technical purposes at certain meteorological stations and with which the ordinary observer need not be concerned.

Before leaving this chapter, some reference should be made to certain instruments of considerable interest used in upper-air weather observation flights.

The strut air thermometer is of the alcohol-in-glass type. The readings are in Centigrade instead of in Fahrenheit, ranging from 55 degrees to minus 35 degrees. Two straps, about 1 inch wide and 2 feet in length, are fixed to the mount, and it is protected from the sun by a sun-shield of polished nickel silver.

Another instrument of considerable importance to the pilot is the air temperature indicator, which is mounted on the instrument board. This is a particularly sensitive and accurate instrument and consists of a fine steel tube, almost as fine as a hair, protected by a braided and water-proofed covering of cotton. The tube is filled with mercury under great pressure, which gives almost perfect precision in its readings.

Another instrument in the same category is the air temperature recorder. This consists of a two-hour clock drum, to which is affixed a chart on which a pen arm travels and records the temperature throughout the 24 hours.

One of the most important instruments in upper-air flights or, indeed, in any aeroplane, is the altimeter. According to the distribution of temperature with height, the movement of the altimeter pointer is in proportion to the changes of altitude, so that the pilot is able to see the approximate height at which he is flying at any time. The instrument consists of one or more boxes held in tension by a strong spring, the boxes being corrugated to give additional elasticity and being on the principle of the ordinary aneroid barometer already described. The metal box relaxes to the tension of the spring as the barometric pressure falls, and reacts conversely when it rises.

The altimeter is set to the barometer readings at sea-level at the beginning of every flight or, in certain cases, at the aerodrome altitude.

Among the less common instruments used by the meteorologist may be mentioned in passing the ozonometer for measuring the amount of ozone in the air, and the electrometer for measuring the amount of electricity in the air. The latter is used particularly during thundery conditions.

Plate 33. *A temporary clearance in the weather being followed by another rain area from the banked-up clouds forming on the horizon.*

Plate 34.   *Altostratus clouds in an irregular layer through which the sun or moon gives a watery appearance and sometimes causes a halo.*

Plate 35. *When clouds of this type increase in size, rain is on the way.*

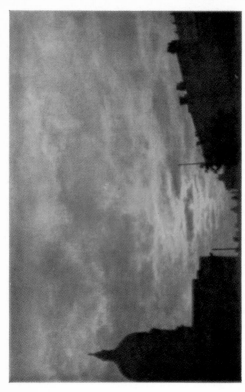

Plate 36. *A frosty winter sunset over the City of London.*

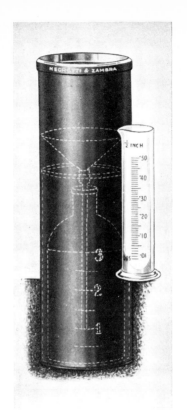

Plate 37. *Rain gauge, with copper funnel and glass
bottle at side, graduated in half-inches of
rainfall.*

Plate 38.   Above: *Bilham screen for sheathed thermometer.* Below: *Large dial velocity indicator
used on control box of large public service
overhead transporters.*

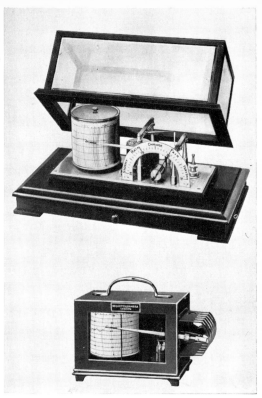

Plate 39. Above: *Recording barograph showing hinged pen arm on clock-driven weekly drum.* Below: *recording thermograph, with weekly clock-driven chart on drum.*

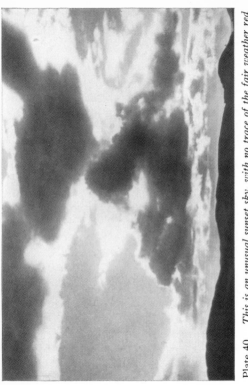

Plate 40. *This is an unusual sunset sky, with no trace of the fair weather red glow. The colourless tone is not a good sign.*

Plate 41. *Clouds breaking up in the west to show a red fine weather sunset, reflected in the lake in foreground.*

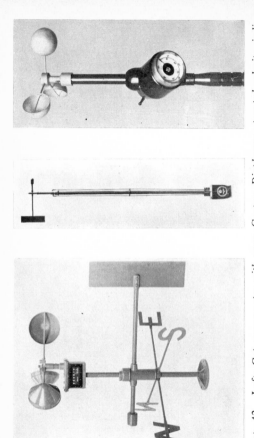

Plate 42. Left: Cup anemometer with vane. Centre: Diaphragm-operated velocity indicator and direction indicator. Right: Hand anemometer.

Plate 43. *Dines' anemograph.*

Plate 44. *Wind speed instrument.*

Plate 45. *Distant reading velocity and directions head used on the "skylon" at the Festival of Britain Exhibition.*

Plate 46.   Top: *Sunshine recorder*. Centre: *Evaporation gauge*. Below: *Cup anemometer*.

Plate 47. *A meteorological assistant adjusting the recording rain gauge.*

Plate 48. *Thunder clouds forming at sunset, reflecting a coppery glint at the edges.*

CHAPTER X

MAKING A WEATHER MAP

THOSE of you who have television sets will be accustomed to seeing the weather map on your screen every evening, giving a brief outline of the present state of the weather over the British Isles and the weather expected during the next 24 hours.

Very few of you, however, probably realise the tremendous amount of work and organisation that is necessary in collecting all the reports gathered from weather observers throughout Britain, northern Europe and the Atlantic Ocean. Let me first tell you how all these reports are collected so far as the British Meteorological Service is concerned.

Some years ago I stood in a small hut, on the rolling Bedfordshire Downs near Dunstable, and watched a thunder-storm going on 2,000 miles away! This hut was part of the Thunder-storm Location Unit of the Central Forecasting Station of the British Meteorological Service (now centred at Bracknell, Berkshire), and is one of the most outstanding inventions of British scientists. Throughout the war it was a closely guarded secret, cleverly camouflaged as a most realistic-looking haystack.

Atmospheric "crackles" coming from lightning flashes which are picked up on our ordinary wireless sets do nothing more than annoy us. But when these same atmospherics are received on specially designed radio direction finders equipped with television tubes, they become items of far-reaching value in forecasting the weather.

There are only four such thunder-storm locators in existence in the British Isles; the other three are in

Scotland, Cornwall and Northern Ireland. They record simultaneously all the main lightning flashes within a radius of 1,500 to 2,000 miles. There is now also a similar network employing stations in Gibraltar, Malta and Cyprus.

On the door of the hut I noticed the international weather symbol for thunder-storms that appears on all charts—a kind of silver zigzag lightning flash. As soon as I entered the hut, black curtains were drawn across the window, and in the semi-darkness a Royal Air Force sergeant sat before the apparatus with earphones fitted, while another member of the staff sat similarly equipped at an opposite table.

The apparatus in front of the sergeant was a receiving screen. In the centre of it was a brilliant spot of light, and for the next five minutes I watched flashes shooting out in small straight lines from this central spot. The exact bearing of each flash is given by a scale marked on the television tube, and as the four stations are linked by private telephones, the control station is able to plot right away the bearing lines on a map.

Where these four lines intersect is the area where the lightning is flashing, and that is the area of the thunder-storms. In this case, I found we had been watching a storm centred over a spot in southern Europe.

The spread and direction of movement of such storms can be followed and sometimes it is possible to forecast thunder-storms over Britain days ahead.

The observers told me that there is not a single day throughout the year when thunder-storms are not recorded somewhere over Europe or the Atlantic. The positioning of these storms during the war was of immense value. When a batch of lightning flashes on the weather map was shown, it meant that severe "icing" would be found in that area, and "icing" was capable of bringing down planes as efficiently as anti-aircraft guns! It also meant that bombing targets were obscured by thick cloud, that electrical disturbances would upset the pilots' instruments, and that treacherous air currents would be encountered.

The Assistant Director told me: "This invention has saved several hundreds of our pilots' lives. At the peak period of the war, about 500 airfields were being so served." The locators are also of considerable value in peace, particularly for civil aviation, for thunder cannot be heard much over 10 miles away, and lightning cannot be seen in the daytime unless it is very near.

All reports of storms are passed on at once to the Communications Room, where they are dealt with. The Communications Room is the vital centre, a hive of marvellous activity. Inward and outward messages are passing continuously all day and night through the hands of a "scrutineer", all reports being in a five-figure code which has been agreed upon internationally. The economy in message transmission can be imagined, when a single figure indicates the state of weather, another figure the force of the wind, another the amount of cloud, and so on.

During the war, it was necessary for every message to be sent by cipher, and therefore it had to be enciphered or deciphered before it left the Communications Room. This was performed by women who had to work at high speed.

It was from here, on the Bedfordshire Downs, that the vital weather forecast for D-day was issued, which led to General Eisenhower postponing the invasion from 5th June to 6th June. For the period just after D-day the Allied Armies in France were entirely dependent upon this Forecasting Centre at Dunstable for all their meteorological information and any delays or inaccuracies in ciphering could have had disastrous results.

The Communications Room as I entered was a sea of heads; girls who had received special training were busy sifting data, editing reports, or compiling broadcasts from information collected from many different sources. They have to ensure that no important data misses its scheduled time on the wireless telegraphy or teleprinter broadcasts.

An officer in the Communications Room showed me a "Sferic" report. ("Sferic" is their abbreviation for "Atmospherics.") It had just been handed in by the Thunder-storm Location Unit. This gave information that storms were in progress over the Alps and off north-west Scotland. "This," he said, "is of the utmost importance to meteorologists in Malta and Iceland who may be briefing captains of air-liners leaving for London or Prestwick."

Wireless telegraphy in the collection and distribution of meteorological data is very little used today, the principal system being a land-line teleprinter, mainly to broadcast completed charts and tables from the Central Forecasting Office. In addition, radio-teleprinter and radio-facsimile are used for overseas.

Just before the end of the war, the average number of weather reports being passed into the Communications Room reached 100,000 every 24 hours. By their devotion to duty in the dull routine of taking down figures (sometimes almost unreadable through bad atmospheric conditions), these men and women provided the vital data without which successful forecasts for major air operations would have been impossible.

Passing on to the Forecasting Room, I was introduced to probably the most important man at the station, the Chief Forecaster. He was a R.F.C. pilot in the First World War, and joined the Meteorological Service in 1919, just before it was taken over by the Air Ministry.

He explained to me the work of the Forecast Branch. Observations are plotted eight times daily over an area from just east of Newfoundland to Russia, and from the Azores and North Africa to Greenland, Iceland and Jan Mayen. In addition, four charts are plotted daily over an area covering the whole of North America and northwards to Spitzbergen. All available information is plotted on the main charts.

From here come the daily weather forecasts for the B.B.C. and the newspapers. Also special gale warnings and forecasts of fog, frost and snow.

"We can give forecasts with considerable accuracy," he said, "up to 12 hours ahead. After 12 hours the degree of accuracy begins to fall, and after 24 hours it's very chancy. You must remember each day's weather is a new problem; no two are ever alike. The main difficulty is timing. We can foresee developments, but they often move faster or slower than anticipated."

The actual and forecast charts are supplemented by written commentaries, and the forecasts fall into three main categories, as follows:

(1) general forecasts for land and sea areas, which go out to the Press and the B.B.C.;
(2) special forecasts for public utility corporations, such as the Central Electricity Generating Board, the gas industry, etc.
(3) longer period special forecasts up to three or four days ahead.

Inquiries for forecasts cover a remarkably wide field, ranging from water supply problems to the sale of ice-cream, and from the building of power stations to the location of convalescent homes. In

1963 the electronic computer Meteor was brought into use for the first time, and now works on an average 68½ hours a week. This has introduced a completely new type of forecasting, and the computer is also used in general weather research, data processing and trials of automatic editing of the synoptic weather reports.

During 1962 as many as 199 stations were carrying out synoptic weather observations in the British Isles, of which 97 were auxiliary stations maintained by the Meteorological Office.

During the war, precision forecasts were at all times essential to Bomber Command to ensure that aircraft arrived over the target exactly at the appointed time and avoided heavily defended localities. On all major operations the Upper Air Section at Dunstable maintained contact with the aircraft throughout the flight, to supply the best possible last-minute estimates of navigational details, temperature (which affects the reading of the air-speed indicator), and wind at the bombing height over the target, by means of which the bomb-sights were set.

Knowing as they did that this Central Forecasting Station was the nerve centre of the British Meteorological Service for the entire northern hemisphere, the Germans did all they could to locate it. But they never succeeded.

Weather observations over the sea are just as vital as land records. As most of our weather comes from the west, the most important sea area for observations is the North Atlantic Ocean, and we were very much handicapped during the last war by lack of information from that direction.

Today there is a voluntary observing ship scheme which supplies reports of the weather at sea. Some ten years ago there were about 450 ships taking part in this scheme; now there are 3,900 ships of all nations, of which nearly 700 are British and about 350 British Commonwealth. They take observations of air and surface sea temperatures, pressure, wind, humidity, visibility, amount, type and height of cloud and period and height of waves at midnight, 6 a.m., midday and 6 p.m. The observing ships are all provided with a barometer, barograph, wet- and dry-bulb thermometers and a special bucket and thermometer for measuring sea-surface temperature.

Although there has been this valuable increase in the number of voluntary observing ships, the official ocean weather stations have been reduced over the past decade for reasons of economy. In 1947 there were 13 weather ships in the North Atlantic, established on a recommendation of the International Civil Aviation Organisation. In 1949 the number was reduced to 10, and in 1954 to 9, of which 4 are British. The information supplied by the weather ships is essential for transatlantic flights and for the supply of forecasts to the Central Forecasting Station, so this economy cut is, to say the least, unfortunate. The present total of 10 is far too few to cover such a vast area as the North Atlantic.

The four British weather ships are based at Greenock, and these are "Castle" frigates (252 ft. in length). They provide the same types of observations as those of the voluntary merchant ships, except that these on the weather ships are hourly, day and night, and not only four times a day. The six-hourly observations are by the launching of a balloon carrying a radar target, which is followed by the ship's radar to a height of 60,000 ft. to take observations of the upper winds. The radiosonde is used for alternate ascents, measuring pressure, temperature and humidity. It comprises a small radio transmitter attached to a balloon made of rubber and filled with hydrogen, which is sent into the upper air. It rises rapidly to a height of about 10 miles, sending messages as it goes. These messages are in the form of a single musical note, the note depending upon the weather element at each level. The signals are received at the base station, where they are converted into the readings of pressure, temperature and humidity while the balloon continues to ascend.

When about 10 miles up, the balloon bursts and the apparatus falls to earth on a small parachute. During its flight, the balloon is blown along with the wind, and by following a radiosonde with direction-finding receivers, the speed and direction of the upper winds can also be found.

Other equipment in addition to the radiosonde includes a fog-measuring instrument, true wind direction and speed indicator, and distant reading sea and air thermographs.

The deputy Marine Superintendent of the Air Ministry Meteorological Office told me that the main purpose of these ships is to provide floating "islands" in the Atlantic from which observations of surface and upper air conditions can be made at regular intervals. This enables a fuller picture of Atlantic weather conditions to be obtained than has been possible up to the present.

Transatlantic aircraft are now able to check their position by taking bearings on these ocean weather ships, and there is also a secondary use in providing air-sea rescue facilities for aircraft and shipping in distress.

"For the men who like ships and the sea, and the study of the weather," said the head of the Marine Branch, "the work is always interesting. It is certainly unusual and, apart from its importance for scientific and practical meteorological purposes, its potential value for the safety of human life is without question."

I talked to a Merchant Navy bo'sun, as he stood on the deck of one of the little vessels, converted from a war-time corvette. "Life is tough on an ocean weather ship. We go out about 300 miles into the Atlantic and stay there for 21 days, hunting the weather. These ships have a terrific roll, and as we are sitting much of the time on 40-foot-high waves, you can guess what that's like! At this time of year (November) especially we have practically no calm days, and more often than not, we are riding heavy southerly or westerly gales."

This weather ship on which the bo'sun was standing was one of those which Britain, together with the U.S.A., is contributing to the International Weather Ship scheme, of which the other countries concerned are Canada, France, Norway, Sweden, Holland and Belgium.

"Each ship," said the skipper, "has 15 days at base, and normally 30 to 34 days at sea, of which 24 days are actually 'on station'. As a rule it takes about 3 days to get there and back. Of course, in very rough weather we are sometimes as long as 5 days on the passage."

A third way in which observations are collected is by the use of aircraft. This, naturally, is concerned with upper air records, which are most important both to the forecaster and to all aerial navigators.

The information that is needed includes such items as atmospheric pressure, temperature, humidity, speed and direction of the upper winds, visibility, height of the bases and the tops of clouds, etc.

One method of collecting this upper air data with radiosonde balloons, which are used for exploring those heights that are beyond the reach of aircraft, has already been described.

"Met." flights, as they are called, carry out weather observations over a very wide area of the North Atlantic. These flights are flown on a triangular track by Hastings aircraft of the R.A.F. Coastal Command, based at Aldergrove. They first fly at a fairly low level (about 2,000 ft.) and then at 18,000 ft. At each position, some 50 nautical miles, they take observations, and at every fourth position come down to take sea-level readings.

In order to see exactly how these flights are carried out, and thus describe them fully, I was taken on one of them as a Press guest. One of the busiest men on the flight seemed to be the Met. air observer. Not only was he responsible for collecting all the records practically non-stop, but it was also his job to check them up afterwards with the readings that had been sent through to the Forecast Room by wireless telegraphy.

As I crouched with him in the somewhat restricted space in the nose of the plane, I noted that one of his assistants was seated at a small table steadily recording the readings of temperature, pressure and humidity at the different levels.

Facing this observer, on his right-hand side, were the three essential instruments for his readings. These were the pressure, altitude and air-speed indicators. Immediately outside his window just in front, fixed on a small bracket, was the psychrometer, which is the name for the thermometer in aircraft. It differs, however, from the more familiar, ordinary thermometer we use at ground-level, and is on the same principle as the wet- and dry-bulb thermometer described in the last chapter. There are two columns of mercury side by side, one having a dry bulb and the other a wet one. The latter is covered by a small piece of cloth called a "sock," which is kept continuously wet by a wick dipping into a small container. As previously explained, the difference in the reading of the two columns gives the humidity measurement, which is particularly important in flying.

As we soared up to the higher levels, away from the cloud and drizzle through which we had been flying at less than 1,000 feet, into the brilliant sunshine and blue sky above, it was possible to see some very fine cloud effects *below* us. A good many detailed cloud observations were now being made, and some photographs taken of the more outstanding cloud formations.

I next paid a visit to the wireless cabin, which had begun to feel very much like a hothouse with the warm sunshine pouring through the glass roof. The two wireless operators (known as "Wops") were seated in their shirt-sleeves, perspiring freely. They had earphones clamped over their heads, and were sending back the many observations to the Forecast Room at base.

The crew of seven comprised the first and second pilots, the air observer, navigator, flight engineer, and the two wireless operators. One of the latter also worked the radar instruments. I learned that each of the crews on these routine Met. flights have to serve for a period of 18 months on the job.

At the completion of our flight, I went along with the air observer to the base station, where he had to go through the regular procedure of checking up his log with the readings that had been sent through to the Forecast Room by wireless telegraphy during the flight. In the room I found them busy plotting all the observations on to a large weather map of northern Europe.

Having a look at the weather map that was evolving, I noted that we had encountered a "low" pressure area over the North Sea, which was now moving south-westwards towards the south-eastern counties, which were undoubtedly in for a dirty day. The forecasters expressed the opinion that there was not likely to be much improvement until the following afternoon, and that before it got better we should probably experience some thunder-storms over that area.

My next visit was to the Operations Room, where I found the station commander inspecting a set of cloud photographs and observations that had come through from the previous flight. There was an immense map that covered the whole of the large wall at the end of the room, which was about the size of an average lecture hall. A girl was plotting on this map, by means of coloured tapes, the courses of the various Met. flights then in progress.

"Briefing" of Met. crews is carried on in this room, and I attended one such "briefing" by the squadron commander. The amount of information was such as to give each member of the crew a very full picture of the general conditions they were likely to meet over the flying area. In addition, the Forecast Room furnished a last-minute estimate of the weather situation ahead of them.

The general public did not realise the value of these Met. flights during the last war, nor the vital part they played in increasing the effectiveness of all operations carried out by Bomber Command. In the earlier days of the war, Spitfires were used, and the pilots not only had to fly their machines and take evasive action from enemy planes, but had also to take weather observations at the same time. The way in which they managed to roll all these jobs into one was to have, strapped to the right knee, a specially constructed weather observation plate, on which was recorded with the free hand all the temperature, pressure and humidity readings, as well as the various cloud formation observations and the checking of the height of cloud bases, etc.

After a while it was found that it was almost impossible to accomplish this one-man job satisfactorily under battle conditions, so the Spitfire was replaced by the Mosquito IV, which then became the standard aircraft for the flights. Subsequently, these planes formed part of the famous Pathfinder Force of Bomber Command.

Until these Met. flights began, we had no means of knowing the weather conditions over the target area, and this was obviously a great handicap to our bombers. The Pathfinder reconnaissance planes, therefore, used to precede the main bomber force, and collect up-to-date information of all the weather conditions in and around the target area. It was the boast of these fine pilots that within 20 minutes of the first warning ring of the telephone they could be airborne and on their way to report the weather conditions at any place within 1,000 miles of base. Even since the war the tradition has held: "Met. Flight takes off in any weather!"

Some extremely important jobs fall to these experienced personnel in peace-time also, such as making detailed reports of the weather for the transatlantic flights of the Queen.

The principal forecasting office for civil aviation is located at London (Heathrow) Airport, and there are other offices at air traffic control centres and civil aerodromes. Meteorological services are, of course, always provided for the R.A.F. and the main forecasting offices are usually at Group Headquarters and function throughout the twenty-four hours. There is normally a senior officer of the Meteorological Office on duty at Command Headquarters. Special forecasting services are provided for R.A.F. aircraft on distant overseas flights, through the interchange of up-to-the-minute information between Great Britain and overseas forecasting stations. The London Airport Forecasting Office now provides information for a number of new airline services to the U.S.A. and West Africa.

Now let us see how all these observations that have been collected are dealt with at the Meteorological Office. Each observer sends in a report for the given hour of the conditions at his station; these are plotted on to the daily weather map with the utmost speed and accuracy, and from the completed map is deduced the forecast for the different districts.

Many people, although they have no professional connection with meteorology, are sufficiently interested in the subject to take these daily weather charts throughout the year. These comprise four pages and contain: (*a*) A weather chart as at 12 noon the previous day, covering most of the northern hemisphere. (*b*) Three other weather charts as at 6 p.m. the previous day and as at midnight and 6 a.m. on the day of issue, covering smaller areas. (*c*) General inference and further outlook. (*d*) Detailed weather reports from land stations in the British Isles and from ships in the North Atlantic Ocean.

For those who are interested in upper air observations in particular, there is also issued a six-page daily aerological record. This contains: (*a*) Nine upper air charts for various levels indicating the conditions from complete sonde readings at midnight and midday on the day of issue. Radio wind readings are given at 6 a.m. and 6 p.m. (*b*) Complete upper air observations from stations in the British Isles and from the four Ocean Weather Ships maintained by Great Britain. (*c*) Notes on the aerological situation.

In order to be able to read a weather report clearly it is necessary to know the various symbols used. Firstly, we should make ourselves acquainted with the weather symbols which are abbreviations known as the "Beaufort Notation." These are as follows:

b	blue sky (i.e. not more than one-quarter covered by cloud)
bc	sky partly cloudy (i.e. approximately one-half covered)
c	generally cloudy
d	drizzle
e	wet air
f	fog (visibility 220 to 1,100 yards)
F	thick fog (visibility less than 220 yards)
fs	low fog over sea (coast stations only)
fg	low fog over land (inland stations only)
g	gloom
h	hail
i	intermittent precipitation
jf	fog at a distance (but not at station)
jp	precipitation within sight of station
KQ	line squall
l	lightning
m	mist
o	overcast sky
p	squalls
r	rain
r_0	slight rain
rr	continuous rain
R	heavy rain
rs	sleet
h(r)	rain and hail
s	snow
ks	storm of drifting snow
k/S	heavy storm of drifting snow (generally low)
k/s_0	slight storm of drifting snow (generally low)
s_0/k	slight storm of drifting snow (generally high)
S/k	heavy storm of drifting snow (generally high)

t	thunder
u	ugly, threatening sky
v	unusual visibility
w	dew
x	hoar-frost
y	dry air
z	dust haze (the turbid atmosphere of dry weather)

It will be understood how these abbreviations supply entries on to the weather reports. A point to notice is that capital letters indicate extremes, such as "R" for heavy rain, and the suffix small "$_0$" indicates slight types of weather, such as "s_0" for slight snow, while repetition indicates continuity, i.e. "rr" continuous rain, "RR" continuous heavy rain.

There is also a code used to show the distance of visibility in different areas, which was given in Chapter VII.

Information necessary to shipping is the state of the sea, and this is also given in code numbers, as follows:

0	calm	5	very rough
1	smooth	6	high
2	slight	7	very high
3	moderate	8	precipitous
4	rough	9	confused

There are also special symbols used to denote particular types of weather on the weather map:

< less than (so many feet), for cloud height

to indicate direction and force of wind, number of arrows indicating force numbers. (*See* Beaufort wind scale further on.)

⊕ solar halo

⌓	lunar halo
⌔	aurora
O	blue sky
◑	partly clouded sky
◍	wholly clouded sky
●	rain
⚥	sleet
✳	snow
△	hail
≡	fog
⊤	thunder
⦧	thunder-storm
∞	slight haze

It will be seen in Fig. xi that the wind arrows all
have feathers. The purpose of this is to show the
force of wind according to the length and number
of feathers. A full-length feather indicates Force No.
2 (slight breeze); a short-length feather, Force No. 1
(light air); one full-length and one short-length,
Force No. 3, and so on. A dead calm is indicated by
an outer circle round the weather symbol circle, thus:

◎	calm, with blue sky
◉	calm, with overcast sky
⊙	calm, with rain falling

Storms are denoted on the weather map by small
black cones, as follows:

▲   North Cone (pointing upwards) to denote
gales starting from a northerly direction.
If a gale starts from east or west, but is
expected to change to a northerly direction, the North Cone is still shown.

▼ South Cone (pointing downwards) to denote gales starting from or changing to a southerly direction.

Temperatures are shown on the British weather map in figures at the places where the readings are observed, and just to the left above the place circle. Just below that is another figure, which is the dewpoint, and between these figures is shown the present weather. Immediately below the place circle is given the height of low cloud in hundreds of feet. To the upper right is shown the barometer change during the past 3 hours, and this is given in millibar tenths, and to the lower right is the past weather. On the place circle is given the amount of total cloud (Fig. x).

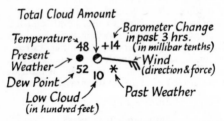

Fig. x. DETAILS OF READINGS WHICH APPEAR ON THE BRITISH WEATHER MAP

These details are only shown on the map of the British Isles section. The larger section that covers the whole of the northern hemisphere only gives the temperature readings and weather symbols, together with the chart of the barometric isobars.

The manner in which the isobars are drawn was explained in an earlier chapter, but here it is possible to see them on an actual weather map (Fig. xi).

If we look at the map on Fig. xi, we will see that the weather situation is such that the isobar lines are drawn in almost a straight line from north to south over eastern England. This is because there is a deep "low" pressure area over the northern Atlantic, reaching across to the Irish coast, and an intense anticyclone ("high" pressure area) over north-eastern Europe. This gives an almost direct south-to-north current of air over eastern England, which lies between the two pressure systems, and a more south-westerly current over western England, Wales and Ireland (which lie nearer to the advancing "low" pressure area). The north-easterly side of this "low" bends the isobar lines slightly to the right, thus setting up a south-easterly wind current over Scotland.

It will also be noticed that there are three separate "fronts"—two occluded fronts over the British Isles, and one cold front cutting across part of Denmark. The relation of the distances between the isobars to the velocity of the wind should also be noted as it may be remembered that in an earlier chapter it was explained that the closer the isobar lines the higher the wind velocity, and vice versa. Here the highest winds, shown by the wind arrows, are seen to be in the Straits of Dover and along the east coast, and on the north-west coast of Ireland.

The weather appears to be rainy over the northern and eastern half of the British Isles, and the whole of Ireland, but there is evidently a temporary improvement over the extreme south-west of the country, confined to Devon and Cornwall, where partially clear skies are shown.

These weather maps, as will be realised, contain

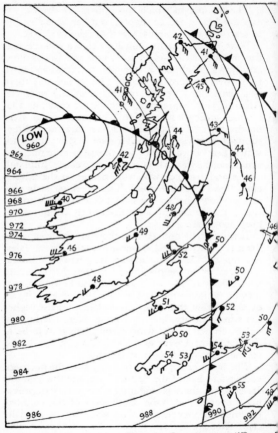

Fig. xi. ISOBARS AND "FRONTS"

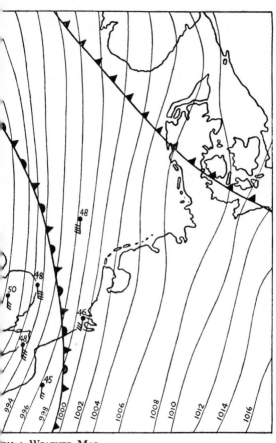

ON A WEATHER MAP

the results of many hundreds of reports pouring into the Central Forecasting Office hour by hour. A fresh map is plotted every 3 hours throughout the day and night, showing the weather situation at midnight, 3 a.m., 6 a.m., and so on. There are also, in addition to these surface weather maps, special supplementary ones on which are plotted the upper air observations at various levels, and these are prepared every 6 hours, from 3 a.m. onwards.

The weather map of the whole of the northern hemisphere is necessary in order to make the 24-hour forecasts for the British Isles, as it is necessary to see exactly what is happening over the Atlantic as well as over the vast wastes of Siberia and the Mediterranean Sea. A complete picture of the whole is essential.

Considerable international co-operation is therefore required. This is made possible by the World Meteorological Organisation, which is responsible for the exchange of information between the various countries. This enables the forecasters in each country to know the existing weather at any station from the Arctic to Africa, and from the American continent to central Russia. It is indeed true to say that the collection of weather reports is independent of political boundaries between nations—except in war-time. The headquarters of the World Meteorological Organisation is at Geneva.

CHAPTER XI

ANIMALS, INSECTS AND PLANTS IN WEATHER RECORDS

MANY country people read the weather signs from observing the behaviour of animals, insects, birds and plants. Although many of the beliefs concerned with such observations are not borne out in fact, it is quite true that certain animals and birds seem to have an intuition of weather changes, and some plants and trees react similarly.

Birds are particularly sensitive to weather changes, and rooks especially so. When they build their nests higher than usual in the trees, it has often been noticed that a warm, fairly dry summer follows. The same applies when they fly high, and the converse is the case if they are seen flying low.

Many country folk maintain that the crowing of cocks in the evening portends coming rain, as does the extra loud chirping of crickets after nightfall. I know of one naturalist who uses his tame toad as a barometer, and he says it is more reliable than the mechanical one hanging on the wall! When a spell of warm, dry weather is approaching, the toad will take up a position on the shady side of the garden (but not if it is only a short one-day spell); when it is about to turn colder, he will fix himself up on the sunny side; when rain is on the way, he will move along to a ledge below the study window.

Many people believe that donkeys start to bray extra loudly if a spell of settled weather is about to break up. To what extent this is borne out by statistics does not seem to have been proved.

Plants are probably on the whole more reliable.

If the leaves wither on the boughs of trees in late autumn instead of falling normally, an extra cold winter frequently follows. Also, when trees are inclined to snap or crack in the autumn it is a proof that the atmosphere is lacking in normal moisture. A dry season may therefore be expected. When the air is damp it softens the leaf stalks of trees, thus putting a strain on them and turning the leaves up, so that they show more than usual of their under-surfaces. This indicates rainy weather approaching, and is particularly applicable to the poplar, lime, plane and sycamore.

There seems a very widespread belief in "The Oak before the Ash" saying:

> If the oak's before the ash,
> Then you'll only get a splash;
> But if the ash precedes the oak,
> Then you may expect a soak.

There is, however, nothing at all in this, and the weather seems to bear no relation to whether the ash precedes the oak, or vice versa. A tree that is a reliable forecaster, however, is the white poplar, which has a downy under-surface that shows its white side when rain is on the way. It is suggested that the cause of this is the upward vertical component in the air movement that is associated with the coming of rain, which renders the under-side of the leaf visible.

When we come to the world of plants we are touching on a more scientific aspect of what is known as phenology. Phenological observations mainly began in 1917 when a record was made of a series of observations on the behaviour of certain plants at irregular hours during the daylight, with notes on the corresponding present and subsequent weather. The results of the survey were both disappointing and surprising, in so far as most of the plants selected did not live up to their reputations as rain forecasters by displaying their opening and closing behaviour.

The plants in question were the scarlet pimpernel, common daisy, common chickweed, white clover, dandelion, gentian, common marigold and blue pimpernel. Temperature at the surface of the soil seems to be the controlling factor in the movements of the daisy, dandelion and chickweed. Daisy and chickweed also respond to changes in the humidity; likewise the scarlet pimpernel, but these three plants only justify their reputations as rain forecasters in so far as the short number of hours which elapse between the increase of humidity and the arrival of rain.

It must not be imagined from this, however, that many plants are not sensitive to coming weather changes, and it merely encourages nature observers to probe more deeply into the subject. The value of our annual phenological observations already described is an example of the importance of plant life in connection with weather changes.

It is obvious that there is quite a close relation between meteorology and botany and that combined observations can be of great value. The study of phenology, however, needs a great deal of patience. It has been found, for example, that cultivated plants and wild plants react to weather in different ways; some of the former will grow satisfactorily only at certain temperatures, and have a definite growth rate at separate stages of the Fahrenheit scale.

Phenology today is considered to be a very important side of meteorology, and is of some considerable interest to the layman who is usually more attracted to the natural history angle than to the more scientific aspect of the subject involving higher mathematics. It is also a natural meeting ground for the botanist who is concerned with plant observations, the entomologist who deals with records of insects, the ornithologist who studies the habits of birds, and the meteorologist who co-ordinates all this data in its relation to weather conditions.

This shows how birds, insects and plants respond to the arrival of warm and cold spells of weather, moisture, drought, and so on. The data for the current year are compared with those of previous years, and from these are deduced the type of weather expected for the coming season. Phenologists assert that birds and insects give a more accurate idea of the approaching weather than plants, and the reason for this is believed to be that plants are affected by past or existing weather to a greater extent.

It is surprising to find what a wide range these reports cover. The observers record the dates on which a large number of plants flower in each particular year at some 450 places in the British Isles, and how they compare with the dates of average appearance; the dates of the first leafing and first colour change of a number of trees, and the first ripening of such species as the horse-chestnut; the first dates of spring and autumn bird migrants, and the first and last song dates; first dates of egg-laying of the song-birds, and the first flying of the young fledglings; the first dates of the appearances of over fifty butterflies and moths; and the first dates of frog spawning.

For many years the noted Rothamsted experimental station has carried out research into the effect of weather on the numbers of insects and the changes in their population figures. It is interesting to note in that direction that observers found that changes of temperature affected insect activity more than any other weather condition. They also found they could measure a relation between the insect populations in any one month and the weather of the previous three months.

Phenological charts are made out in much the same way as weather charts, with their isobar lines and figures. In these charts, however, the lines are not called isobars. The lines of equal flowering dates of plants are termed Isophenes, and the lines of equal divergence from the average flowering date are termed Isakairs.

There is no doubt that the systematic use of a nature calendar, based on these accurate phenological reports, would not only increase general interest in our countryside, but also dispose of many popular fallacies.

It should also encourage amateur observers to contribute more useful data of bird, insect and plant behaviour in relation to weather conditions.

CHAPTER XII

THE AMATEUR OBSERVER'S
LOG-BOOK

IT is generally admitted that the amateur meteorologist has made a valuable contribution to weather research. These observers, although not professionals, are accepted as Fellows of the Royal Meteorological Society if their research work and general interest in the subject is serious and sincere.

In this category of non-professionals should be included our volunteer observers throughout the country. It is not generally realised that the monthly report of the Meteorological Office is based very largely on the observations of volunteers, in addition to such official observers as the Town Clerk, Borough Engineer, Medical Officer of Health, Pier Master, Lighthouse Keeper, and so on. There are only a certain number of stations who possess these official observers; the remainder rely entirely on volunteer observers who are keen and efficient amateur weather watchers.

The amateur weather enthusiasts, however, must set about the job properly, using accurate instruments and taking the greatest care in recording their correct readings. It can be a most engrossing hobby, but even a hobby should be done well and thoroughly.

The first point to consider is what instruments you must have for your minimum requirements.

A thermometer and barometer are obviously among the necessary ones. It is not likely that you will feel inclined to incur the expense of a standard pattern screened thermometer, nor is that necessary.

An ordinary self-recording maximum and minimum thermometer will serve the purpose.

The temperature readings must be made regularly, at fixed hours, and although these hours must to a certain extent be arranged to fit in with the watcher's other business, the most preferable hours are 7 or 8 a.m., 1 p.m., 6 or 7 p.m. and midnight. The maximum and minimum columns must be set each morning and night for their automatic recording of these temperatures, which provide a fairly good approximation to the day's mean temperature. If you are absent at those hours you should arrange for someone else to take and record these readings for you.

As regards the barometer, when I first commenced observations, I used an ordinary aneroid, but later I found it worth while investing in a barograph, which enabled me to look back at the weekly records over the year, and did away with the necessity of taking individual observations at set hours.

You may not be fortunate enough to have a weather vane on your house, nor to be within sight of one over any large building. In that case never trust to smoke from chimneys that might be influenced by local currents of air. It is better to watch the wind direction from the clouds.

If you can run to a rainfall gauge, and/or a sunshine recorder, so much the better, for it will enable you to complete your observations more fully. Even without these, however, you can record a fairly clear picture of the weather through the years, as I have done, by the use of only the most simple instruments.

Now to come to the matter of compiling your actual log-book, which should be entered up every day. As an example I have taken a sample page out of one of my own daily weather diaries.

EXAMPLE OF DAILY WEATHER DIARY

Date	Barometer		Thermometer						Wind
	7 a.m.	10 p.m.	7 a.m.	1 p.m.	6 p.m.	10 p.m.	Max.	Min.	
Dec.									
1	29·50	29·42	44	48	46	45	49	42	S.W.
2	29·35	29·50	43	47	47	44	48	42	S.W.
3	29·75	29·92	40	44	42	38	44	37	N.W.
4	29·95	29·90	33	41	41	41	41	32	N.W.
5	29·78	29·60	40	46	46	45	46	39	S.W.
6	29·43	29·30	45	46	44	40	47	40	S.E.
7	29·55	29·80	36	39	36	32	39	32	E.
8	29·97	30·05	29	33	31	28	34	27	E.
9	30·20	30·32	25	31	28	26	32	24	N.E.
10	30·35	30·30	18	29	25	22	29	18	S.E.
11	30·24	30·15	16	27	22	17	28	15	S.E.
12	30·00	29·88	26	33	31	30	33	25	S.
13	29·75	29·60	34	40	42	42	42	33	S.
14	29·52	29·47	42	46	45	44	47	40	S.W.
15	29·20	29·13	47	49	48	48	50	46	S.W.
16	29·05	29·25	46	47	45	44	48	44	S.W.
17	29·50	29·83	37	44	39	35	44	34	N.W.
18	29·92	29·77	31	40	42	44	44	30	N.W.
19	29·52	29·65	45	48	44	40	48	40	S.W.
20	29·90	30·15	32	35	32	30	35	30	E.
21	30·33	30·55	27	31	29	26	32	26	N.E.
22	30·60	30·62	24	26	24	22	27	21	N.E.
23	30·50	30·37	21	26	26	26	26	20	S.E.
24	30·12	29·95	30	37	39	40	40	30	S.

Note—Temperatures at or below freezing are here shown in bold type but in the diary are entered in red.

118

Weather

Fair early, then rain from 10 a.m. onwards; generally gusty.
Dull and rainy, after rough night; some improvement late in period.
Mainly fine and sunny, with short afternoon shower.
Fine sunny morning; becoming overcast after midday; drizzle at night.
Very dull and damp; drizzle at times.
Overcast day, with some drizzle; fine evening.
Overcast all day; strong wind.
Overcast and windy, occasional snow eddies.
Mainly overcast; some snow showers; wind falling towards evening.
Foggy morning and night; clear sky overhead; some sunshine midday.
Thick fog all day.
Foggy early, then clearing with increasing cloud and breeze.
Very overcast with drizzle at times; gusty.
Rain all day; wind increasing.
Half gale, with heavy rain at times.
Very rough, with intermittent rain.
Showery, sunny intervals; fine night.
Foggy early, then sunny; rain in evening.
Heavy rain early; then dull and drizzling.
Overcast; very keen wind.
Dull and cloudy; moderate wind.
Mainly overcast; wind falling towards evening.
Foggy morning; clearing towards evening.
Fair and misty at first, increasing cloud later, rain in evening.

The barometer readings can be entered in your daily weather diary direct from the barograph twice a day—say, at 9 a.m. and 9 p.m., or three times—7 a.m., midday and 10 p.m.

You will also note the day's weather in descriptive form—or by the symbols used by the Meteorological Office (as tabulated on pages 102–105), the direction of the wind; the amount of sunshine (if this is possible), and the amount of rainfall (if you have a small rain-gauge).

These observations can, of course, be extended. Later on I found it very useful to note the types of sunrise and sunset, as it is at these times that significant indications are given by the sky observations. The cloud abbreviations, as set out by the official meteorological symbols, may be used in most cases (with whatever descriptive amplification may be necessary), so that very little additional space need be taken up in your diary.

The really keen weather observer compiles at the end of each month a summary of the general conditions that have been experienced. Here again I produce a page from my own weather diary that gives an example of such a monthly summary.

If the month has recorded any outstanding temperatures or similar features, a graph will prove an interesting supplement. The graph can also be used for comparison purposes, either in comparing the month with the same month of the previous year, or with the mean temperature of the month over the period of records.

In the same way, at the end of each year I have always made a point of compiling an annual summary which includes the last frost date of the spring and the first frost date of the autumn, comparing these with previous years. Similarly, I also make a point of noting the date of the winter's first snowfall,

Plate 49.   *A member of the R.A.F. Met. staff filling the wet-bulb psychrometer.*

F.P. 120

Plate 50.   *The hoisting of a gale-warning cone.*

Plate 51. *A meteorological assistant recording the readings of instruments.*

Plate 52.   *Sending up a radiosonde balloon.*

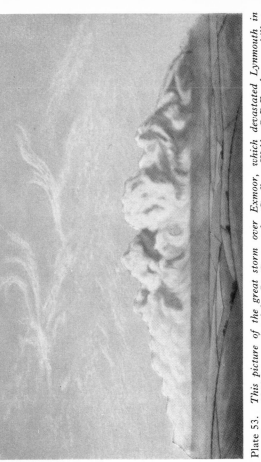

Plate 53. *This picture of the great storm over Exmoor, which devastated Lynmouth in 1952, was painted by Lt.-Commander Geoffrey Webb, O.B.E., from a hilltop over forty miles away.*

Plate 54. *A meteorological assistant reading instruments.*

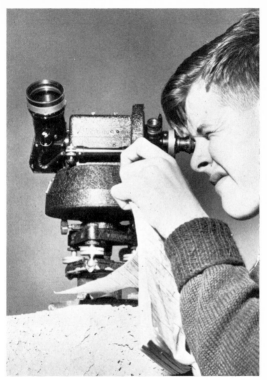

Plate 55.   *Tracking the path of a pilot balloon with a special theodolite. This enables speeds and directions of the upper winds at various levels to be determined.*

Plate 56.   *Plotting observations on a weather chart.*

Plate 57. *Two red sunsets appearing in each case after a day of storm, denoting improving weather on the morrow.*

Plate 58. Above: *Briefing a crew before a weather routine flight.* Below: *Forecasters at work on the preparation of flight forecasts.*

Plate 59. *Plotting air Met. flights in the "Operations" room.*

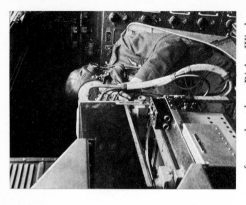

Plate 60.   Left: *The observation table in the nose of a weather plane.*   Right: *Wireless telegraphy operator in a weather plane.*

Plate 61. Above: *A meteorological forecaster briefs a civil airline crew for an impending flight.* Below: *A routine weather observation flight.*

Plate 62. *Ocean weather ship "Weather Reporter" with a plane carrying Christmas supplies.*

Plate 63. *Studying incoming weather from the Atlantic.*

Plate 64. Top: *An angry dull red of storm diffusing the clouds.* Below: *The clear red hue of a fine sunset.*

EXAMPLE OF MONTHLY SUMMARY

December

Maximum temperature 50°—15th

Minimum temperature 15°—11th

Mean maximum temperature 44°

Mean minimum temperature 30°

Mean temperature 37°

Mean daily range 8°

Absolute range 14°—18th

Maximum-reading of barometer 30·62″—22nd

Minimum-reading of barometer 29·05″—16th

Mean-reading of barometer 29·83″

Number of days:

When wind between N. and E. —6

When wind between E. and S. —6

When wind between S. and W.—15

When wind between W. and N. —4

When dead calm   2

When wind force 1—5

When wind force 2—7

When wind force 3—6

When wind force 4—2

When wind force 5—5

When wind force 6—3

When over force 6—1

Number of days on which rain fell—21

Number of days on which snow fell—2

Number of days on which fog recorded—7

Number of days on which thunder heard—1

Total amount of rainfall—3·2 inches.

Total number of hours' sunshine—38 hours.

General remarks on month's weather:

Mainly mild and wet, but with two wintry periods of short duration, i.e. from 7th to 12th, and from 20th to 23rd. First cold period accompanied by slight snow. Gales on 1st, 15th, 16th, 30th and 31st. Fog mainly slight, except on 11th, which was dense. Thunder heard on 16th, but no lightning reported seen.

and the last spring snowfall, together with the number of days on which the ground was covered with snow in the district under observation (as contrasted with the number of days on which snow actually fell).

All weather diaries should have notes of the topographical features of the district where the records are being kept; height above sea-level, nature of soil, if sheltered or open position, and any other details that would be likely to have a bearing on the weather there.

The way in which the work of the amateur weather observer is recognised was emphasised by Sir Richard Gregory when he gave his presidential address to the Royal Meteorological Society during the inter-war years. He said:

> "It should be remembered that some of the most important of these [voluntary observations] represent research undertaken purely for the love of the subject and, therefore, appropriately described as the work of amateurs. Though the word 'amateur' is commonly used disparagingly to signify a superficial student or worker, its correct meaning is one who loves or is fond of anything or cultivates a subject as a pastime, as distinguished from one who prosecutes it as a professional occupation."

He added that there should be no conflict of interests between the amateur and professional meteorologist. They are joined together with one interest in common—that of the advancement and extension of meteorological knowledge.

Keen amateur meteorologists can now build their own satellite cloud picture receivers. The National Aeronautic and Space Administration is publishing a booklet giving details of how to construct such a station for about £200.

CHAPTER XIII

WEATHER FORECASTING PROBLEMS

NOT infrequently we read in our papers that we may expect a spell of settled weather for the next few days, and then—to our disgust—the very next morning we wake up to rain. It is perhaps only a natural reaction that we should abuse those who have been responsible for preparing the forecasts.

But the layman does not realise the extreme complexity of our weather over the British Isles. In a maritime country like this, occupying the position that it does between the Atlantic Ocean and the vast land areas of eastern Europe, the whole weather situation may change quite suddenly in a matter of hours.

The chief forecaster of the Central Forecasting Station has admitted that very little degree of accuracy can be guaranteed for any forecast issued for more than 24 hours ahead. He told me that the problem which has so far proved insurmountable is the direction and speed of "low" pressure systems coming in from the Atlantic.

The evening's synoptic chart may show such a system approaching directly from south-west to north-east, on a diagonal line across the British Isles. The obvious forecast would be for the rain area to be centred over the western and northern part of the country, leaving the south-east corner fine and dry, under the influence of a "high" pressure system over France. But then, for no apparent reason, the "low" may suddenly change its course and turn south-east, bringing all the rain to the Channel coast and south-eastern England, and leaving the north quite fine.

Again, the direction that has been plotted on the weather maps may prove to be correct, and the "low" will follow the course expected. But the time of its arrival has been estimated on the speed at which it has been travelling so far, so that the next day's forecast gives us rain from early morning. Then, after we have cancelled a proposed outing that day, it turns out exasperatingly fine and sunny! What has happened is that—again for no apparent reason—the "low" has suddenly slowed up on reaching Cornwall, and from there travels eastwards so slowly that the rain arrives in London at night instead of in the morning, as expected.

Recently attempts have been made to forecast the general type of weather in the British Isles for a month ahead. The method adopted has been to match the past month as closely as possible with that of one or more previous years in the 80 years' record of weather, in anticipation of the coming weather fitting the previous patterns. This has not proved very successful, and the Meteorological Office, in their report for the year ending 31st December 1962, state: "The method is reasonable in principle but not always reliable in practice, perhaps because the matching of conditions between different years is not close enough, and certainly it is often difficult or impossible to find really close analogues".

In some parts of the world the weather follows a more uniform pattern, and the rain seasons arrive each year on fairly regular dates. Certain places also have regular weather cycles, an example of which is the 4-year cycle of rainfall and temperature in parts of Australia.

In the British Isles the cycle most familiar to most people is known as the Buchan periods, and we read very often in our daily papers that a "Buchan cold spell" is due. A good deal of misconception has arisen over this, however, as with so many other weather beliefs. Buchan worked out these cycles of weather observations he made in Scotland, and they were therefore intended to apply to that country in particular, and not to the British Isles as a whole.

Some of the "Buchan spells," nevertheless, do occur over England as well as Scotland during most years, and the most reliable are his cold spell of 8th to 16th February, his hot spell of 12th to 15th July, and his warm spell of 1st to 5th December.

All attempts to find some regular recurring periods of similar weather over the years in the British Isles have met with comparative failure, with one exception. That is a cycle of weather that has certainly kept fairly near to form over the past few centuries, and is known as the Bruckner cycle.

When Dr. Eduard Bruckner was Professor of Geography at Berlin, he made a very detailed record of rainfall, barometric pressure and temperature over a long period of years, from which he discovered that between the years 1020 and 1890 there had existed 25 cycles of recurring weather, of an average length of 34.8 years.

This 35-year cycle, as it came to be known, followed a regular pattern over some of the centuries, but at intervals broke down and varied between 30 and 40 years. Then it would suddenly return to its regular periodicity again. Last century it seemed to settle down again, and we experienced very severe winters at 35-year intervals, i.e. 1860, 1894–5 and 1929–30. It will thus be interesting to see if 1964–5 keeps up the cycle.*

Some parts of the British Isles have certain very local weather cycles. Of these the best known are the 3·1 years' rainfall recurrence at Oxford; the 5·1 years' period of cold winds at Southport, Lancs.; and the 11.4 years' cycle of temperatures in Edinburgh. There is also a heavy rainfall cycle of 11 years at Rothesay, Bute, which is considered to be due to the south-west wind frequencies which become most pronounced every 11 years in the western Highlands.

The most detailed research this century into the subject of weather cycles was conducted during the war, when in 1941 the noted meteorologist, Dr. C. E. P. Brooks, and a team of scientists launched a concentrated study of western Europe's climate. Dr. Brooks centred his research mainly on any possible recurrence in pressure distribution, and synoptic charts were examined for the preceding 52 years.

The results of this research have provided some valuable data for the weather student, and may be summarised quite briefly as follows.

It was found that over the 52-year period pressure distribution fell into four main seasonal groups, which give an extremely useful guide to the average weather over western Europe.

---

* Weather data going much farther back than man-kept records have been obtained through the measurements of tree-rings. They are made on cores taken from growing trees by means of a specially devised auger. Each of these cores has a thin section shaved off and mounted between sheets of glass, very much on the principle of an ordinary lantern slide. By projecting these on to a ground-glass screen, they are magnified to a degree sufficient for measuring with greatly increased accuracy.

The value of these tree-ring measurements is to establish cycles of rainfall and drought years, because the rings of rainy years are comparatively thick, and those of dry years correspondingly thin.

(1) October to early February: mainly stormy periods with minor "high-pressure" interludes.

(2) February to May: series of cold waves associated with "high-pressure" systems over northern Europe.

(3) Summer months: incursions into western Europe of polar maritime and tropical maritime air alternating with some regularity.

(4) September to early October: spells of anticyclonic conditions ("late summers").

It was found that most of the stormy periods were associated with depressions moving across the coastal areas of north-western Europe, and penetrating into Scandinavia or the Baltic. The fine spells were due to anticyclones forming in polar air moving southwards, or to the Azores anticyclone (so regular in the summer months) extending north-eastwards.

It is interesting to note that the most definite recurrence is the mid-February cold spell that is associated with an outbreak of cold polar or continental air, because this coincides with the most reliable Buchan "cold spell."

Dr. Brooks is of the opinion that these recurrences do not arise by chance, and gives his expert conclusions on the causes. He considers there is a bearing on the different annual variations of temperature over continents and oceans where—in winter—the land masses and the air over them cool rapidly, while the surfaces of the oceans remain relatively warm. This results in a pool of cold air collecting over Europe, which, however, eventually becomes unstable and breaks out towards the Atlantic as a stream of cold air. At that stage the whole process begins all over again, and hence the weather recurs in the same sequence.

There may eventually be achieved some better success in long-range forecasting if the Brooks researches can be continued and extended, coupled with much greater knowledge of the higher levels of the atmosphere.

Everything else in Nature moves in regular rhythm, so why not weather? Can we get data sufficiently far back into the past to establish whether our climates have swung backwards and forwards between rainfall and drought, between warmth and cold, like a pendulum? Over the centuries long-range forecasting has been called the "Everest" of meteorologists; now that this great peak has been conquered by man, perhaps it is a good omen.

Every extension in the field of weather research must be one step forward in the advancement of forecasting knowledge. All the developments of recent years, including wireless telegraphy, the invention of radiosonde, the measuring of upper winds by radar, etc., have helped to advance the subject.

The Meteorological Office emphasises how important it is to distinguish between a forecast and a prediction.

Prediction implies a great deal of precision, leaving very little element of uncertainty, and is more applicable to astronomy than meteorology. The date and time of the next new moon, the next eclipse, and so on, can be *predicted* by astronomers. A meteorologist, however, can only *forecast* coming weather, because the element of uncertainty is comparatively high. A forecast, therefore, is a scientific estimate of the probability of a forthcoming event.

The Meteorological Office divides the degrees of certainty as expressed in their forecasts into four different classes:*

* *Your Weather Service*, H.M. Stationery Office (1s. net).

(a) The first or highest degree of certainty is that in which no qualifying word or phrase is used, e.g. "fine today," "rain tomorrow," "winds will be westerly."

(b) The second degree of certainty is indicated by the terms "expected," "probable" or "probably," "likely" or "likelihood of."

(c) The third degree of certainty is indicated by the terms "prospect of," "indications of," "conditions are favourable for."

(d) The fourth degree of certainty is indicated by the terms "may be," "may occur," "chance of," "perhaps," "possible" or "possibility of."

It is well to keep this classification before you when reading or listening to your next day's forecast.

A well-known meteorologist has said that to be able to forecast the course of coming events one must be able to see in the present occurrence the form of the future fact. That is the basis upon which all weather researchers work.

Of recent years some scientific attempts have been made in different parts of the world to control the weather. Some of these have been partially successful, others complete failures.

Russian scientists have been using artillery shells to introduce cloud-seeding chemicals into hail-storms, and have been successful in reducing hail damage by up to 80 per cent and reducing the size of hailstones from 5 cm. to 1 cm. This has encouraged Canadian and U.S.A. scientists to begin similar experiments, as the losses to crops through hail damage amounts to over £100 million annually.

In Poland a new low-level weather rocket has been developed by the Rocket and Satellite Department of the State Institute for Hydrology and Meteorology. This rocket is to be used in experiments for either modifying or dispersing clouds.

CHAPTER XIV

CLIMATES OF THE WORLD

When we speak of the climate of a certain country, we are often too inclined to think about it in terms of temperature only. We all know that the Equator means heat and the Arctic means cold. But a climate is the normal character of its weather over the centuries; its rain and sunshine, winds, storms, and everything that goes to make up the various characteristics that we have been reading about in the foregoing pages.

If we confined climate to temperatures, it would be quite impossible to divide off the different latitudes into temperature zones, for places of similar temperatures wander far afield from places of equal latitudes. For example, Edinburgh is pretty well as near the North Pole as Moscow; London is actually farther north than Winnipeg; and Cornwall is practically on the same latitude as Newfoundland.

From this we can understand that climates are not governed by their northerly or southerly latitudes, but by continental, oceanic and topographical considerations.

The great continental land masses develop extremes of heat and cold; coastal climates are tempered by the equalising effect on temperature caused by the oceans; and topographical features, such as hills, mountains and valleys, forests and plains, all affect the climates of the particular places concerned.

We all know how the Gulf Stream affects our own climate, which would otherwise probably be about as cold as Greenland. In the same way, the Labrador

Current affects Newfoundland in the opposite way, for this is a cold stream that carries the icy waters of Baffin Bay to that coast, and gives it winters of Arctic temperatures in spite of its being—as we have already found—on about the same latitude as Cornwall!

Even in the same countries the climates may vary. In our own relatively small islands, there are several distinct climates. We are familiar with the winter snows of Scotland's Highlands and the English Midlands; the rainy climate of south-west Scotland and Cumberland; the dry weather of East Anglia; and the warmth of Cornwall. All this different weather is associated with the respective climates of separate areas of the British Isles.

Let us now take a look at the world's climates, which are divided up into three main zones—Arctic, Temperate and Torrid, which in turn are again sub-divided into smaller zones.

Arctic. This consists of the Sub-Arctic, having more than 6 months below 40° F.; and Polar, which has no warm season at all throughout the year.

The Sub-Arctic zone embraces the area from northern Canada right across to Iceland and thence to northern Scandinavia, central Russia and the Sea of Okhotsk, with a southern belt through the South Shetlands and South Orkneys.

The Polar zone covers the Arctic and Antarctic oceans and continents. In the north it is bounded by a line drawn through Labrador, north Iceland, Kara Sea, south-east Siberia and central Alaska; and in the south by Graham Land, Enderby Land and Clarie Land (all of which may be traced on any world atlas).

Temperate. This comprises three zones: the Mid-temperate, consisting of a climate similar to that of Britain; the Warm-temperate, having no month below 45° F.; and the Cool-temperate, with from 3 to 4 months below 45° F.

The Mid-temperate zone is bounded by a somewhat curving line, that encloses a belt embracing the British Isles, central Europe, narrowing into a waist at western Asia to New York, and widening out again in the North Atlantic.

The Warm-temperate zone is enclosed in one belt along the southern boundary of the Mid-temperate, running through the southern part of America, Morocco, the Mediterranean, southern China, and across to California. A second belt runs through central Argentine, Tristan da Cunha, Cape of Good Hope and southern Australia.

The Cool-temperature zone is enclosed in one belt running from the south of Newfoundland to the Faroes, and across southern Scandinavia southeastwards over the Caspian Sea to the Sea of Japan. A second belt runs from the Falkland Isles across to the south of New Zealand.

Torrid. This consists of the Equatorial, where the mean annual temperature is above 70° F., and the Sub-tropical, with no cold season, and no month below 50° F.

The Equatorial, as its name implies, lies within a belt across the Equator, and encloses territories on each immediate side of it. This belt runs across central Africa, Panama Canal, Sandwich Islands and Borneo.

The Sub-tropical borders each side of the Equatorial zone, being bounded on the north by the Suez Canal, Himalayas, Nanking and the Gulf of California; and on the south by Polynesia, Bolivia, South Africa and central Australia.

The Equatorial climate is of two types; the continental, which has a prolonged dry season, and the marine, which has no definite dry season at all. There is a very regular uniformity of temperature, which keeps around the 80° F. average throughout the year, and the mean annual range is no more than from 3 degrees to 5 degrees.

The monsoons, which are a feature of the tropics, are mostly experienced on the eastern side of large land areas. In India, the winter monsoon lasts from October to March, whereas the summer monsoon is mainly during June.

The five great deserts have somewhat different climates, those in the high latitudes having a colder winter season. The Sahara is one of the hot deserts, but it has a very large diurnal range of temperature, sometimes as much as 60 degrees between day and night. The other four are the Arabian, Australian, Atacama and Kalahari deserts.

Coming to the Temperate zones, the most familiar is the Warm-temperate of the Mediterranean, which has a much more varied climate than any of the Torrid zones. The summer is fairly dry, the warmest month having a mean temperature of between 70° F. and 80° F. The winter has more rain, which diminishes in quantity towards the south. The coldest winter month has a mean temperature of from 45° F. to 50° F. There is a high percentage of sunshine.

The western coast of America, which comes within this zone, is somewhat similar to the climate of Britain. In the summer the coastal temperature averages about 60° F., but is considerably higher inland. The prevailing winds are westerly.

The South American climate, which also comes within this zone, varies a good deal. Coastal temperatures keep around the very pleasant level of 67° F. to 70° F., but the rainfall ranges from as low as 4½ inches in one place to 105 inches in another!

Another area that just falls within the Warm-temperate zone is the extreme tip of South Africa. The mean January temperature of Cape Town, for example, is about 68°F. The total annual rainfall is no more than about 25 inches, of which about 20 inches fall in the winter months, so the summer is fairly dry; indeed, four summer months have less than 1 inch.

A portion of southern Australia also comes into this zone. Perth, with its ideal winter mean temperature of about 55°F. and a summer made pleasant by the prevailing sea winds, is a most comfortable climate in which to live.

The Cool-temperate zone of northern China, which takes in Peking and the Korean peninsula, has quite a cold winter, with 4 months of mean temperature below freezing. The summer temperatures rise to 80°F. or just above. Japan, also within this zone, has a more varied climate. The island of Yezo, immediately north of Tokyo, has 5 months with a mean temperature below freezing, whereas the two small southerly islands, Shikoku and Kyushu, have no proper winter at all, with the mean temperature above 40°F.

The extreme south of New Zealand, in this zone, has the coldest month just below 43°F., and rainfall is fairly evenly distributed throughout the year, while the sunshine compares favourably with that of the Mediterranean.

The northern American sector of this zone has an inland winter temperature that is almost continuously below freezing, with a summer mean of just above 70°F. On the coast, however, the climate is much more temperate. A feature of the summer months is the almost daily occurrence of thunderstorms.

The Cool-temperate zone in Europe includes

the continental and maritime type of climate, and is therefore very varied, with a temperature range of from under 30° F. to over 60° F. Rainfall is heaviest in the west and decreases eastwards, whereas the sunshine decreases westwards.

In the Arctic zones, we come to the typically continental climate of Canada, which falls within the Sub-Arctic sector. In the centre of Canada, Winnipeg has a temperature below zero for 2 months. The temperatures in the vicinity of the Great Lakes are less extreme, owing to the moderating influence of the expanse of water. Slightly warmer in winter than central Canada is southern Labrador, also within the same zone.

In the European portion is Scandinavia, which has very low winter temperatures inland, but comparatively mild ones the whole way up the coast. Rainfall in Sweden is very low.

It may be surprising to find that Siberia comes within this Sub-Arctic zone, rather than in the Polar zone, as its winter climate is extreme, with temperatures well below zero. But in the summer the thermometer rises over 80° F., with means as high as 70° F.

Finally there is the Polar sector of the Arctic zone. The winter months have unbroken frost, although for a short summer period temperatures will rise above freezing.

The summer thaw usually lasts from June to early September over most of the Arctic, but even during those months the mean is just below 50° F. Fog is a frequent feature of both Arctic and Antarctic, and, on the other hand, so are blizzards that reach a wind velocity of 150 miles per hour!

There is a January *mean* temperature of *30° F. below zero* in the Mackenzie Valley of Canada, with extremes of up to 100 degrees of frost. Point

Barrow, in northern Alaska, has a January mean of 19°F. below zero and a July mean of 40°F. above. North-east Labrador has a January mean of 6°F. below zero, and a July mean of 47°F. above.

The northern Europe islands of Spitzbergen, Nova Zemlya, Jan Mayen, within this Polar zone, all vary somewhat. Spitzbergen minimum mean is 2°F. below zero in the mid-winter months, and 40°F. to 42°F. above in midsummer. Jan Mayen is a good deal milder, with a mid-winter mean of 24°F., but the summer is cooler with a mean of only 42°F. in the hottest month (July), and only 33°F. in August.

For some time Russia has been considering a scheme for damming the Bering Strait, so as to change the north polar climate. Cold Arctic water would be pumped into the Pacific, causing the Gulf Stream to flow across the Arctic Ocean and remove the ice there.

There is admittedly a risk here, if such a scheme should be put into action. The rise in sea-level could very well flood many big low-lying cities.

The Antarctic is a much more Polar climate than the Arctic. Here there is no summer, and no period sufficiently without frost to allow of the growth of vegetation, such as is possible in the Arctic. (The only exception is the tip of Graham Land, south of the South Shetland Isles.)

So we complete our survey of the world's climates, from which we are able to appreciate the distinction between "weather" and "climate," proving the truth of the schoolboy's remark that "climate lasts all the time, weather only a few days."

CHAPTER XV

WEATHER LORE

FROM among the hundreds of old weather "saws" only a few have any foundation in meteorological fact. One of the truest of all proverbs is:

> Red in morning, shepherds' warning;
> Red at night, shepherds' delight.

You may remember that the same proverb appears in different wording in the Bible, when Christ said:

> When it is evening, ye say, it will be fair weather, for the sky is red. And in the morning, it will be foul weather today, for the sky is red and lowering.

These words have stood the test of centuries. There is also a good deal of truth in the proverb:

> Rain before seven,
> Fine before eleven.

It very often happens that a small trough of bad weather will start in the early hours of the morning and will usually clear within 6 or 7 hours at the most. We are all familiar with the pale watery-looking sunset that denotes coming rain, or after sunset an equally watery moon or one with a halo round it.

> Last night the Sun went pale to bed,
> The Moon in haloes hid her head . . .
> 'Twill surely rain—I see with sorrow,
> Our jaunt must be put off tomorrow.

Another true "saw" is:

> Mackerel sky and mares' tails
> Make tall ships carry low sails.

This type of sky, described in the chapter on clouds, which often looks very much like a mackerel's back or the brush of a mare's tail, is always a fore-runner of bad weather—both wind and rain.

Some of the old "saws" are very difficult to kill in spite of the lack of any evidence of their being borne out. One of these is that the weather changes with the moon, or that "when the new moon holds the old moon in its arms" bad weather is at hand. The correct one relating to the moon and the weather is this:

> Moon and weather
> May change together,
> But a change of moon
> Does not change the weather.

Another familiar couplet about the moon relates to when one sees a halo around it:

> The bigger the ring,
> The nearer the rain.

This is quite true, for, as we have learned in a previous chapter, when a rain area approaches, a ring or a halo is formed due to refraction by ice crystals of the high cirrus clouds.

Due to the same cause, the smaller stars will become dimmed and look as though they are inclined to huddle in misty clusters round the larger ones. This also precedes rainy weather:

> When the stars begin to huddle,
> The earth will soon become a puddle.

Many people still persist in believing the St. Swithin's Day fallacy, namely, that if it rains on that day (15th July) it will rain for 40 days after. The weather on any particular day of the year has no bearing on the succeeding ones. Although there is no truth in this, the legend has an interesting origin.

St. Swithin, Bishop of Winchester, was buried at his own request in a plot of ground just by the church wall, where water from the eaves might always drop in benediction on his grave. But a century later, when he was canonised, it was decided that his body should be removed from this grave into the church, upon which his spirit decreed as a protest that it should rain without ceasing for 40 days, to delay the removal.

The couplet connected with Candlemas also is no truer:

> If Candlemas be fair and clear
> There'll be twa winters in the year.

The saints seem to have rather a bad reputation as regards the weather. In addition to St. Swithin, the preceding month—June—has several "rainy" saints. One of these, St. Medard, Bishop of Noyon, is another of the 40-days' type:

> St. Medard's drops drop forty days.

St. Faustus has a similar reputation, while St. Vitus (15th June) is not only connected with the ailment of that name, but also with being a noted rain-maker!

A saying that is actually based on scientific data is:

> Fast runs the ant as the mercury rises.

An American scientist, Dr. Harlow Shapley, director of the Harvard College Observatory, investigated the movements of ants under varying temperatures. He found that the higher the temperature, the more swiftly they moved, and, conversely, that when it was colder they moved more slowly. His research was carried to such a degree of accuracy that he was able to estimate the temperature to within 1° F., merely by working out the different speed of ants, and drawing up a relative timing chart.

Another accurate saying is:

> As the days grow longer
> The cold gets stronger.

The cooling effect through winter months is cumulative, so that very often some of the severest frosts are experienced in February.

A familiar couplet concerning the rainbow is:

> Rainbow in the morning, shepherds' warning;
> Rainbow at night, shepherds' delight.

This is generally correct, as we are only able to see a rainbow when the sun is behind us and a rain shower in front. This means that when we see a rainbow in early morning the rain is to the west and is approaching us, whereas a rainbow in the evening must be seen in the east and the rain area has therefore probably passed away.

Neither of the sayings, "February filldyke," nor "March, black ram, Comes in like a lion and goes out like a lamb," is to be relied on.

Two couplets about the barometer may be taken as generally true:

> First rise after low
> Foretells a stronger blow, *and*

> Long notice, long last,
> Short notice, soon past.

As regards the first, when the barometer has fallen very low its first rise is usually accompanied by a very high wind. As to the second saying, it is certainly a fact that if the barometer goes on falling for 2 or 3 days during a settled spell without any break in the weather, the unsettled period will usually last much longer than if there was a sudden quick fall of the barometer. In other words, the longer the warning the longer the change of weather will continue.

If we study the Bible we may be surprised to find how many weather prophecies are to be found there. There are several concerning the south wind. It is a fact that the most serious storms come out of the south, on a south-easterly or south-westerly wind. In three Books of the Old Testament reference is made to this: "Out of the south cometh the whirl-wind" (Job xxxvii. 9); "As whirlwinds in the south" (Isaiah xxi. 1); "And shall go with the whirlwinds of the south" (Zechariah ix. 14).

But south winds also bring heat-waves in the summer months, and turning to St. Luke (xii. 55), we read: "When ye see the south wind blow, ye say, There will be heat; and it cometh to pass."

A "rain sky" usually forms and spreads from the west, and in fine weather—if the western sky gradually becomes clouded over, and an unbroken greyish film spreads across—rain is not very far distant. Thus we read in St. Luke (xii. 54): "When ye see a cloud rise out of the west, straightway ye say, There cometh a shower; and so it is."

It is generally known that a period of drought comes in on an east wind, which is truly confirmed in Hosea (xiii. 15): "An east wind shall come, the wind of the Lord shall come up from the wilderness, and his spring shall become dry and his fountain shall be dried up." Likewise, in winter an easterly wind current heralds an influx of severe weather, and "Shall it not utterly wither, when the east wind toucheth it?" says Ezekiel (xvii. 10).

An east wind, however, is often much maligned, especially as regards the couplet "When the wind is in the east, 'tis neither good for man nor beast." Although an east wind admittedly can be very trying in the winter, especially for elderly people, it will often in the summer herald a long spell of warm sunny weather.

GLOSSARY

Altitude. Height above sea-level.

Anemometer. Instrument for measuring velocity of wind.

Anticyclone. An area of high pressure (fine weather).

Atmosphere. A gaseous envelope, surrounding the earth.

Barograph. Instrument for recording rise or fall of atmospheric pressure.

Barometer. Instrument for measuring atmospheric pressure.

Bora. A cold wind in the Adriatic Sea.

Cirrus. A high layer of cloud.

Cold Front. A mass of air which is formed when cold air moves forward and pushes warm air out of its path.

Continental Air. A mass of air which has its source over a large area of land.

Corona. A single ring or several rings encircling the sun or moon that sometimes precedes unsettled weather.

Crepuscular Rays. Lines of watery light that appear to radiate from the sun, often seen before a shower.

Cumulus. A white puffy cloud often associated with showery weather.

Cyclone. An area of low atmospheric pressure that rotates clockwise in the southern hemisphere and counter-clockwise in the northern.

Dewpoint. The temperature to which any given mass of air is cooled to raise its humidity to 100 per cent.

Electrometer. Instrument for measuring amount of electricity in the air, used especially in thundery weather.

Evaporation. Difference between the readings of the wet and dry bulbs of a thermometer.

Evaporimeter. Instrument for measuring degree of evaporation.

Fohn. A wind in the Alpine villages which carries an excessive dry heat.

Freezing Level. The height above the ground at which water will freeze.

Freezing point. 32° Fahrenheit.

Front. A surface in the atmosphere which divides two masses of contrasting air.

Haboob. A dust-storm of the Sudan.

Halo. A misty circle or series of circles around the sun or moon preceding the advance of a rain area.

Harmattan. A sand-storm originating over the Sahara desert.

Heavenly Cross. A sun pillar that is crossed by a horizontal bar.

High. An abbreviation for an area of high barometric pressure (fine weather).

Humidity. The amount of water vapour in a given mass of air.

Hurricane. A tropical cyclone.

Hygrometer. An instrument to measure moisture in the atmosphere.

Inversion. A level in the upper atmosphere where the usual decrease of temperature with altitude is reversed.

Isobar. A line drawn on a weather map through a series of places that have equal readings of barometric pressure.

Isotherm. A line drawn on a weather map through a series of places that have equal readings of temperature.

Khamsin. A hot, dry, dust-laden wind in Egypt.

Low. An abbreviation for an area of low barometric pressure (rain area).

Maritime. A term applied to an air mass whose source is over a large expanse of ocean.

Meteorology. The study of weather.

Mistral. A cold wind that blows through the Rhône Valley.

Mock Sun. A sky phenomena giving the appearance of a second fainter sun at the side of the real one, caused by a cirrus cloud on occasions.

Nimbus. The rain cloud.

Occluded Front. A combination of two "fronts," either a cold front lifting a warm front or a warm front lifting a cold one.

Ozone. A gas, on and above the earth's surface, each of whose molecules consist of three atoms of oxygen.

Ozonometer. Instrument for measuring the amount of ozone in the air at any particular place at a given time.

Phenology. Nature records, including dates of flowering of plants, leafing of trees, arrivals of bird migrants, etc.

Radio Sonde. A small balloon attached to an instrument for taking soundings in the upper air.

Ridge. An area of high barometric pressure of greater length than width, and therefore shaped like a ridge, which usually divides two areas of low pressure.

Sirocco. A hot, dry wind which blows along the Mediterranean.

Stratosphere. The position of the earth's atmosphere next above the level of the troposphere.

Stratus. A type of cloud that often drifts across hilltops in parallel layers or combines with other types of cloud.

Sun Pillar. A vertical column of light sometimes seen extending above and below the sun, caused by the reflection of the sun's rays on the vertical sides of crystal columns in the atmosphere.

Superior Air. A mass of air whose source is in the upper troposphere.

Synoptic Charts. Weather maps.

Thermograph. Instrument for recording the temperature.

Thermometer. Instrument for measuring temperature.

Troposphere. The portion of the atmosphere lying next to the earth's surface that reaches up to the base of the stratosphere.

Trough. An area of low pressure with greater length than width, and thus shaped like a trough, which usually lies between two areas of high pressure.

Warm Front. A frontal surface formed when warm air is advancing and pushing cold air before it.

Wave. A small bend in a stationary front.

Willy Willy. A miniature tornado peculiar to Australia.

APPENDICES

Appendix I

COMPARISON BETWEEN BAROMETER SCALES

Inches	Millimetres	Millibars
27·0	685·0	914·6
27·5	697·4	931·5
28·0	711·2	948·2
28·5	723·9	965·1
29·0	736·6	982·0
29·5	749·3	999·0
30·0	762·0	1015·9
30·5	774·7	1032·8
31·0	789·9	1053·1

Appendix II

BAROMETRIC PRESSURE AT VARIOUS HEIGHTS

Height Feet	Pressure Inches	Millimetres	Height Feet	Pressure Inches	Millimetres
0	29·921	760·00	20,000	13·749	349·25
500	29·384	746·35	21,000	13·183	334·90
1,000	28·856	732·95	22,000	12·637	321·00
2,000	27·821	706·65	23,000	12·112	307·55
3,000	26·817	681·15	24,000	11·596	294·60
4,000	25·842	656·40	25,000	11·104	282·05
5,000	24·896	632·35	26,000	10·628	269·95
6,000	23·979	609·05	27,000	10·169	258·30
7,000	23·091	586·45	28,000	9·726	247·05
8,000	22·226	564·55	29,000	9·298	236·20
9,000	21·388	543·30	30,000	8·886	225·70
10,000	20·577	522·70	31,000	8·489	215·65
11,000	19·792	502·70	32,000	8·106	205·90
12,000	19·030	483·35	33,000	7·738	196·55
13,000	18·292	464·65	34,000	7·383	187·55
14,000	17·578	446·50	35,000	7·041	178·85
15,000	16·888	428·95	36,000	6·712	170·50
16,000	16·220	411·95	37,000	6·396	162·50
17,000	15·572	395·45	38,000	6·097	154·85
18,000	14·944	379·55	39,000	5·811	147·60
19,000	14·336	364·15	40,000	5·538	140·70

Appendix III

TEMPERATURE, FREEZING-POINTS

Acetone	freezes at	−139° F.,	− 95° C.
Alcohol (Ethyl)	freezes at	−179° F.,	−117·3° C.
Mercury	freezes at	− 37·8° F.,	− 38·8° C.
Pratt's Petrol	freezes at	−198·4° F.,	−128° C.
Sea Water	freezes at	28° F.,	− 2·2° C.
Fresh Water	freezes at	32° F.,	0° C.

Appendix IV

TEMPERATURE, BOILING-POINTS

Alcohol	173° F.,	78·3° C.
Ether	94° F.,	34·5° C.
Mercury	674° F.,	356·7° C.
Nitric Acid, pure	186·8° F.,	86° C.
Sulphur	832° F.,	444·6° C.
Water	212° F.,	100° C.

(at baro. 29·995 inches, 761·9 millimetres, temperature 62° F., 16·7° C., latitude 51° 28′.)

Sea Water	212·9° F.,	100·5° C.

TEMPERATURE, THERMOMETER SCALES COMPARED

1 degree Centigrade is equal to 1·8 degree Fahrenheit.
1 degree Fahrenheit is equal to 0·56 degree Centigrade.

Fahrenheit	Centigrade	Fahrenheit	Centigrade	Fahrenheit	Centigrade
32·0	0	69·8	21	105·8	41
33·8	1	71·6	22	107·6	42
35·6	2	73·4	23	109·4	43
37·4	3	75·2	24	111·2	44
39·2	4	77·0	25	113·0	45
41·0	5	78·8	26	114·8	46
42·8	6	80·6	27	116·6	47
44·6	7	82·4	28	118·4	48
46·4	8	84·2	29	120·2	49
48·2	9	86·0	30	122·0	50
50·0	10	87·8	31	123·8	51
51·8	11	89·6	32	125·6	52
53·6	12	91·4	33	127·4	53
55·4	13	93·2	34	129·2	54
57·2	14	95·0	35	131·0	55
59·0	15	96·8	36	132·8	56
60·8	16	98·6	37	134·6	57
62·6	17	100·4	38	136·4	58
64·4	18	102·2	39	138·2	59
66·2	19	104·0	40	140·0	60
68·0	20				

INDEX

SBN 7232 0064 5
PRINTED FOR THE PUBLISHERS
BY JARROLD AND SONS, LTD, NORWICH
1518.1169